BUILDING HISTORY--HISTORY BUILDING

THE LDS CONFERENCE CENTER AND ITS HISTORY

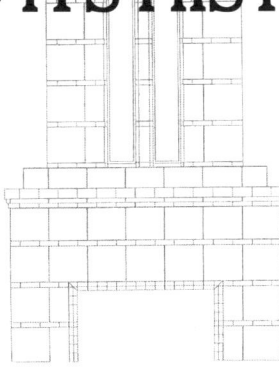

W. Dee Halverson

DMT Publishing

HERITAGE ASSOCIATES, INC.

W. Dee Halverson
Martha A. Halverson

Book Design & Layout
Amy Robinson

Transcriptions
Christie J. Halverson

DMT Publishing

Copyright © 2000 by Heritage Associates, Inc.
7942 Excelsius Circle
Salt Lake City, Utah 84121
heritageassoc.com

ACKNOWLEDGMENTS

We wish to thank the many people and organizations that helped make this book possible: J. Randy Okland, Alan S. Layton, Ted M. Jacobsen, and James G. Peterson at Legacy Constructors; Thomas E. Hanson, Leland L. Gray, Kerry B. Nielsen, and Gary Holland at LDS Special Projects Department.

For their patience in answering untold technical questions during tape-recorded oral history interviews with the author, we wish to thank: Thomas E. Hanson, Leland Gray, Kerry Nielsen, Gary Holland, J. Randy Okland, Alan S. Layton, Ted M. Jacobsen, Ben Nilsen, George Ambrose, Lonnie Bullard, Harvey Wright, James G. Peterson, Blake Dallin, Dick Shipley, Paul Sandberg, Chris Bardin, Robert Frasca, Joseph Collins, Laurie Olin, Susan Weiler, Leonard Auerbach, Patty Glasow, Christopher Jaffe, Nathan Charlton, Ted and Dallas Orchard, Marty Gibbs, David Miller, Guy Moore, Gary Barlow, Paul Fetzer, Jack Bethards, Ben E. and Bradley Banks, Mark Eubank, Jay Starley, Roger Gukeisen, Steven Watterson, Jack Jensen, Chris Evans, and Paul Seppi.

For their invaluable contribution in providing the course-of-construction photographs we thank: Jed A. Clark, Manager Photo Services; Craig W. Dimond, Lead Photographer Photo Services; Matthew T. Reier, Photographer Photo Services; Louise Goddard, Sr. Clerk Photo Services; and Tamra Hamblin Rotieta, Photographer Photo Services at the LDS Photo Services and Visual Resources Library.

Our gratitude also goes to Tim Hunt, Mark Manser and Kent Woodruff of DMT Publishing for their vision and faith in the project from beginning to end.

CREDITS

The following have provided photographs: Legacy Constructors / LDS Photo Services, Utah State Historical Society, W. Dee Halverson, Mrs. Jane H. Dudley, Dallas Orchard, Gary Holland, Chris Evans, and The Peninsula (Washington) Daily News.

Architectural drawings and renderings courtesy of LDS Special Projects Department.

PREFACE

October 5, 1999 was my fifty-third birthday. My wife, Marty, and I were driving home to Salt Lake City from a brief family visit to Seattle. As we were leaving Baker, Oregon the mobile telephone rang. We were both surprised and anxious at the same time since we only used this phone for emergency contacts with our family members. Our daughter Amy's cheerful voice quickly dispelled our fears when she told us that Alan Layton had called to see if I would like to research and write the story of the LDS Conference Center and its construction for publication by April 1, 2000!

Then it hit me— why not look for and write about the human and artistic messages found in all historic buildings? This had been a major theme of my graduate studies in England at the University of York. This was the prime message of one of my most influential mentors, Sir Bernard Feilden. In his heroic restoration work on St. Paul's Cathedral in London and the York Minster, Sir Bernard had demonstrated that all classic buildings of any age contained messages of their construction techniques and materials. You only have to look closely for them— depicted in the stained-glass windows, hand-carved choir stalls, stone work and even on the faces of limestone gargoyles.

In 1988 during an international symposium on the Salt Lake City & County Building, I invited Sir Bernard to see at first-hand how an historic landmark was retrofit with an earthquake-mitigating base isolation system. As we toured the vintage structure while the work was still under way and many of Salt Lake City's religious and secular buildings, Sir Bernard pointed out to me the human and artistic messages left by workers nearly a century earlier. "See," he said, "these are the same kind of clues that I have found in all historic buildings. It doesn't matter whether you are in a 1,000-year-old house of worship or a 100-year-old municipal seat, the worker's messages are there to be read and studied. An historic building is one that gives us a sense of wonder and makes us want to know more about the people and culture that produced it."

This recollection helped me to formulate a methodology that

would be successful in telling the story of an historic building— one that was still being built. I decided to conduct a series of oral-history interviews with those who decided to build the Conference Center; those who would design, engineer, and plan it; those who would be its master builders and craftsmen; and finally those whose hands would create it from the day of its ground breaking to the day of its dedication. These would be the voices who would tell the story of the Conference Center.

The construction of the LDS Conference Center has touched and softened hearts of those I would call hardened workers, or as they call themselves "construction stiffs". Men would actually get choked up during the interviewing and to have to wait, to compose themselves before they could continue.

I've sensed emotional feelings while discussing the extraction of granite in Little Cottonwood Canyon in what many call the "miracle of the stone." Those very same feelings were apparent to me as I asked the designers how they came up with the idea of how to soften the impact of a six- acre roof top that is essentially flat. Instead of putting the heating and cooling equipment, they designed something very unique. I consider their design to be a direct fulfillment of a prophesy that Brigham Young gave in April, 1853 as the pioneers were laying one of the chief corner stones of the Salt Lake Temple. He told the crowd there that he had, ever since 1847, five years earlier, envisioned the Temple as it would appear, not with one spire, but with six. Then he went on to refer to another building on which roof there were ponds, and groves of trees.

Brigham Young's words were fulfilled by Robert Frasca and Laurie Olin, a couple of architects from Portland, Oregon and Philadelphia, Pennsylvania. They were inspired as they sat on the McCune Mansion steps, looking over the site. They envisioned six acres of trees, fountains, streams and planted areas on the roof of the Conference Center.

President Hinckley expressed a sense of urgency concerning the Conference Center. He shocked everyone at the groundbreaking when he said, "We will be opening this building in April of 2000." My research has led me to believe that all of these workers-- the Legacy Constructors, the design team, the supervisors, right down to the men hanging the sheet rock, doing the painting, or hanging the doors— eventually got the picture. They were willing to sacrifice Saturday afternoon soccer games with their families to be available to work in the last minute sprint towards the finish.

W. Dee Halverson

October 5, 2000

INTRODUCTION

In the years ahead we will come to realize the miracle what the conception, design, and construction of the Conference Center represents. In a little more than 1,000 days this magnificent and unique structure has risen on a 10-acre block north of Temple Square. From its ground breaking on July 24, 1997 to its dedication during the LDS General Conference in October, 2000 more than 4,000 men and women have worked together to create a modern-miracle from steel and stone.

The Conference Center with its 1.4 million square-foot interior, including a 21,000-seat auditorium, is now one of the world's largest religious buildings. It stands as a witness of the Lord's promises to the members of The Church of Jesus Christ of Latter-day Saints. The story of its construction is more than a story of architects, engineers, builders, and special consultants— it is one of vision, faith, and determination.

In his opening day comments on April 1, 2000, President Gordon B. Hinckley said:

"The Conference Center will prove to be a great addition to this city. Not only will our general conferences be held here, and some other religious meetings, but it will serve as a cultural center for the very best artistic presentations. We hope that those not of our faith will come here, experience the ambience of this beautiful place, and feel grateful for its presence. We thank all who have worked so hard to bring it to this stage."

"Therefore, when we build let us think that we build forever. Let it not be for present delight, nor for present use alone; let it be such work as our decendants will thank us. Let us think, as we lay stone on stone, that a time is to come when those stones will be held sacred because our hands have touched them and that men will say as they look upon the labour, See! This our fathers did for us."

--John Ruskin,
British essayist (1819-1900).
Seven Lamps of Architecture, VII, 186.

CONTENTS

ACKNOWLEDGMENTS & CREDITS..3

PREFACE..4

INTRODUCTION...6

CHAPTER 1:   BREAKING GROUND (1997)..8

CHAPTER 2:   A MIRACLE IN PROGRESS (1998)..58

CHAPTER 3:   AGAINST ALL ODDS (1999)..114

CHAPTER 4:   SPRINT TO THE FINISH (2000)..170

CHAPTER ONE

1997
BREAKING GROUND

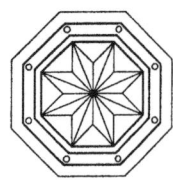

On a beautiful morning, July 24, 1997, thousands of Utahns, together with state and local government leaders joined with President Gordon B. Hinckley and other General Authorities of The Church of Jesus Christ of Latter-day Saints for a special and sacred event. It was the groundbreaking ceremony of the LDS Conference Center in Salt Lake City, Utah. Following remarks by Governor Michael Leavitt, Mayor Dee Dee Corradini, President James E. Faust and President Thomas S. Monson of the LDS First Presidency, President Gordon B. Hinckley gave the following address:

"My beloved brethren and sisters. What a wonderful occasion this is. On this 24th of July, 1997, we turn our faces from celebration of the past to celebration of the future. We're here for a good while, we're going to be. This Church is growing rapidly across the world. We have outgrown some of the facilities which we have.

FACTS & STATS

- The Conference Center will seat 21,000 and the Small Theater will seat 905.
- Frame of building constructed of reinforced concrete with steel roof frame.
- 1.4 million square feet in area (the Church Office Building has 850,000 sq.ft. of area).
- There are 13 passenger elevators, 12 escalators, and 3 service and stage elevators.
- 1,300 spaces in underground parking garage.
- Designed to seismic 4 specifications.
- Central spire feature on roof - 92 feet tall.
- Legacy Constructors used nearly 100 subcontractors and 4,000 workers on-site.

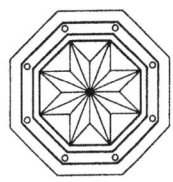

"The building which we propose to build here will seat about 21,000 people. That's three times the capacity of the present tabernacle. And that I submit is a very significant number for a house of worship. This will be a thing of beauty. This will be a great structure which will complement the wonderful buildings on Temple Square. It will be oriented to the south. It's access will be the access of the temple and it will, as it were, look toward that great and sacred structure.

"You may be interested to know that back in 1940 the brethren very seriously considered what we have now determined to do. They actually had the Church architect draw up some plans of an assembly building. They projected that it would stand on this block. They talked about it and about the re-creation of the Salt Lake Theater and Social Hall as places of amusement and entertainment and the arts. The numbers among [the brethren] who spoke on behalf of the fact that we never could accommodate all who might wish to come. Those voices prevailed and nothing ever came of the thing. That building as they envisioned it would have seated 10,000 on the main floor and 9,000 in a circular balcony.

"I think we will build a more beautiful building, a more distinguished building, a more utilitarian building and a building in which there will be a greater refinement of the spirit felt. This will be a magnificent structure. It will cost a lot of money. I'm grateful to say that through the great faith of the Latter-day Saints, we have the means with which

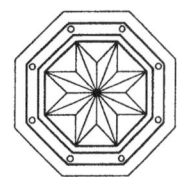

to build it. I hope we will not waste a single penny. I hope we will be prudent and wise and careful and that the outcome of all this will be a structure of which we can be proud and of which I believe the Lord will be proud. His name will be spoken frequently within this hall. His name will be worshiped as will the name of his beloved son, our Savior and Redeemer and the voices which speak in this hall will be carried across the world to the nations of the earth as this Church goes on and continues to grow from it's present membership of 10 million, scattered in more than 160 nations, to numbers beyond our ability to calculate and to places beyond our ability to guess at this time.

The old Tabernacle was built in 1852 as a simple adobe meeting house for about 3,000 people. It was used until 1877, when it was torn down to make way for the construction of the Assembly Hall. (Courtesy of Utah State Historical Society)

"We have been a building people. When the Saints first came here they built a bowery. . . with a framed roof and brush, willows, and some evergreen materials to shield them from the sun. They built the Old Tabernacle where the Assembly Hall now stands. They built the new Tabernacle. They built the Assembly Hall. They built the Salt Lake Temple and great and marvelous is the concept of that remarkable Temple Square. Now we

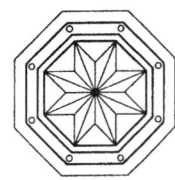

hope that this [new Conference Center] will complement all of that and will add very substantially to it. This will be a place for General Conference. This will be a place for other meetings. This will be a place of the arts. It will be built as well as we know how to build in this season of the history of the world and I hope that it will stand for as long as the earth lasts and serve the purpose of the Kingdom of God.

"I feel very good about that which we're undertaking. I think Brigham Young would smile and be pleased with what we do. I think his successors in office would all be pleased. I think those who discussed such a structure in 1940, President Grant and counselors and the Council of the Twelve would be pleased that

The Salt Lake Temple prior to its dedication in 1893.
(Courtesy of Utah State Historical Society)

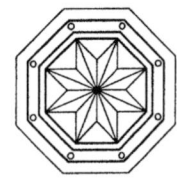

we're now taking this significant step and I think those who come after us will be grateful for what will be accomplished here on this square.

"This is a great and marvelous occasion and somehow I just feel that it is so fitting and so proper that on the 150th Anniversary of the arrival of our people in this valley, we break ground for this new building. It is a thing of which we can be proud and I think when we occupy it and dedicate it, our hearts will be filled with gratitude and appreciation and thanksgiving for what has been accomplished. The architect and the builders have promised me that it will be ready for use for the April conference of the year 2000, so you can put that in all your journals and hope it comes to pass. We have a consortium of three great contracting firms [Jacobsen, Layton and Okland] in this valley who will put this together."

Later President Hinckley would give the following address as a farewell to the Tabernacle on Temple Square, as well as an introduction to the new Conference Center:

"My brethren and sisters, as we conclude this great conference, we experience considerable emotion. If present plans hold, this is the last time we will meet in this Tabernacle for general conference. With few exceptions, a half-dozen perhaps, for 132 years our conferences have been held here.

"This Tabernacle was conceived in 1863 and was first used for the October 1867 conference. There was no gallery in the building at that time. This was added for the

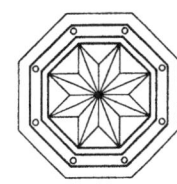

April Conference of 1870. What a remarkable structure this has been. But it has grown too small for our needs. At the time of its building it was a tremendous undertaking, built to accommodate all who wished to attend conference. It replaced the old Tabernacle, which was built to the south of us and which seated about 2,500.

"We salute President Brigham Young on his boldness in undertaking the construction of this unique and remarkable building at a time when this was still frontier territory. The concept of the design was original. Its builders knew of nothing else quite like it. . . . It has served the needs of this Church and this community through all of these years. The voices of prophets have spoken out from this podium. . . . Presidents of the nation and other

The Tabernacle was begun in 1863 and designed to seat about 6,000 people. The building has been in continuous use since October, 1867. (Couresty of Utah State Historical Society)

distinguished men have spoken from where I now stand. This has been home to the Mormon Tabernacle Choir since the structure was completed. . . . It was the first home of the Utah Symphony. Handel's *Messiah* has been presented here over a period of many years. Countless concerts of various kinds, a variety of musical ensembles, and many distinguished soloists have all entertained the public in this

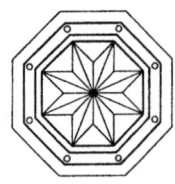

great and singular hall.

"The new hall, which we are erecting on the adjoining block and which we have named the Conference Center, will seat 21,000— with its adjoining theater, 22,000— nearly three and a half times the capacity of this Tabernacle. I do not know if we will fill it, but I do know that we have spoken to much larger gatherings of Latter-day Saints. For instance, in Santiago, Chile, we spoke to 57,500 in a great football stadium; in Buenos Aires, Argentina, to 50,000; in Manila in the Philippines, in a great coliseum, we spoke to 35,000 gathered under one roof.

"The new hall will take some getting accustomed to. But it will be more pleasant. It will be air-conditioned. The seating will be more comfortable than these hard wooden pews. My fear is that too many will fall asleep. It is not of the same design as this Tabernacle, but it is also of a unique and wonderful kind. It represents the very latest in architectural and engineering skills.

"We anticipate that next April 2000 we will meet in a new hall as we usher in a new century and a new millennium. This building may not be complete at that time. The organ probably will not be finished. There will be other construction details needing attention. It will likely be dedicated a year from this conference.

"It is a very large and a truly magnificent structure, designed and built to the highest seismic codes. It is constructed with reinforced concrete with a granite veneer.

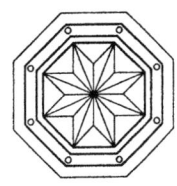

That granite is the same stone that was used in the building of the Salt Lake Temple, including the blemishes which you will recognize in both buildings. . . . It is a bold step we are taking. But this boldness is in harmony with the tremendous outreach of the Church across the world.

"We have no desire to out do Brigham Young or his architects— William H. Folsom, Henry Grow, and Truman O. Angel. We wish only to build on the tremendous foundation which President Young laid in pioneering this marvelous work here in the valleys of the West. As today we close the doors of this Tabernacle and look forward to opening the doors of the new Conference Center next April, we do so with love, with appreciation, with respect, with reverence— really with affection— for this building and for those who have gone before us, who built so well, and whose handiwork has served so long. . . ." (General Conference, October 4, 1999)

In 1994 President Gordon B. Hinckley (then first counselor to President Ezra Taft Benson) called in Ted Simmons of the Church's physical facilities office and Leland Gray, a Church architect, and told them of a special project he wanted them to work on. It was time to consider the design of a building to replace the Salt Lake Tabernacle which had served well since 1868, but which couldn't meet the needs of the LDS Church during its bi-annual General Conference sessions.

PLANNING FOR THE CONFERENCE CENTER

Leland Gray has been a senior designer and an area architect for The Church of Jesus Christ of Latter-day Saints since 1978. He has served as a special projects architect for the Church since 1994 when he was asked to work directly with President Hinckley on the preliminary design and final development of the Conference Center. Gray made the following comments on January 6, 2000 about his early involvement in the initial architectural and engineering plans for the Conference Center:

"About 6 years ago, long before the Conference Center was publicly announced, I was working with Ted Simmons, who has passed away now. He headed the planning and construction of all the Church's physical facilities at the time. Ted told me that President Hinckley had a special project that he wanted us to work on. And so we began the process. There were just four of us involved, Ted, myself, the President, and his personal secretary. We spent about 2 years studying alternative methods of building such a building.

"We presented to President Hinckley five different concepts of how this building could work, one of which was very similar to the building we've got now. All the

configurations of the large theater/auditorium itself have changed very little and we settled on a structural system. Because of economic reasons, we elected to go with a concrete thin shell structure. We worked with a company out of Texas and a group of engineers out of Texas that specialize in doing that type of building. It's not an uncommon kind of building, and the largest thin shell in the world is the Mericana Stadium in Sao Paulo, Brazil. It has an immense span. It seats 165,000. The reason we looked at going that way was economy. A building like that goes up incredibly quick. It's actually built with an air form. For well over two years the design was a thin shell. It had tremendous structural advantages. It's virtually immune to fire, to earthquake, and the wind, but it's not very attractive. It looks like a dome no matter what you do.

"My role was to make sure that when we were through we had produced a building that was an LDS building, and that it felt comfortable not only to the President, but to the members of the Church. We had been given direction at different times along the way by various leaders of the Church. Elder Packer had made a statement, 'The members of the Church should feel at home in this building.' I don't think he meant that it should look like the Tabernacle, but we've tried to make a building that feels like a church, not like an arena or coliseum. We came back with the recommendation that we use Bob Frasca and his architectural firm in Portland. The Bishopric agreed and said to move on this. We went to Bob's firm and indicated

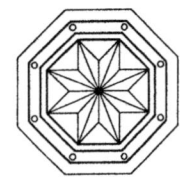

to them that though we had a list of selected consultants, we felt like it had to be their decision who they wanted to use as consultants because they would be ultimately responsible for coordinating the project.

"Bob Frasca came to the site and stood on the steps of the McCune Mansion, and to study the plan as I had proposed it and its orientation on the site. He got the vision in his mind as he stood on the McCune Mansion steps that he had to produce a building that would complement rather than compete with what was already there. We had a design constraint on the site as is typical. Design constraints that bother you in the beginning usually wind up to be your best friend. In this case it was a 75 foot height limitation established by zoning. This building design, in its full configuration with a fly loft would have needed to approach 180 or 200 feet, but we were limited to 75 feet. We had the advantage of having a steep site so we could dig a monstrously deep hole and take a lot of the height of the building and bury it in the ground. Bob's idea was to put a park on top of the building.

"At one of our meetings President Hinckley invited his counselors to comment freely about the project. I remember the comment being made to him, 'President we have overflow capacity right now in the Tabernacle. We can go over into the Assembly Hall. We can go over into the Joseph Smith Building. We've got many locations where

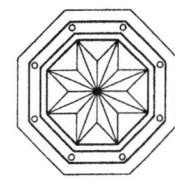

we can overflow to and we're broadcasting to millions of people throughout the world.' And he kind of leaned back in his chair and he thought for a moment, listening carefully to what was said. Then he said, very thoughtfully, 'It's not the same.'

"Then the statement was made, 'President, this will be a tremendous sacrifice for the Saints.' He simply said, 'This won't be the sacrifice for us, that the temple was for them.' I was overwhelmed by his determination, his dedication and his vision to what this building was going to provide for the Latter-day Saints of today and the future.

"Fairly early on in the design process President Hinckley said to me one day, 'How am I going to justify the extreme expense of this building for conference twice a year?' I said, 'President, that depends on how you look at it, but there are other things we could do in this building.' And he said, 'Why don't you come back and tell me what some of those things could be.'

"Kerry Nielsen and I worked together to produce some boards with some proposed ideas of things that could be done in the building, but with the implication that this couldn't be the same building that we had been talking about up to that point. It would need to change. In order to accomplish musical performances beyond congregation or choir singing, to get concert type performances, you need a totally different set of acoustics. We talked about the fact that if we decided to do any kind of stage performances, whether it be opera, pageants, plays, whatever, it would

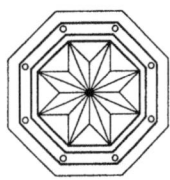

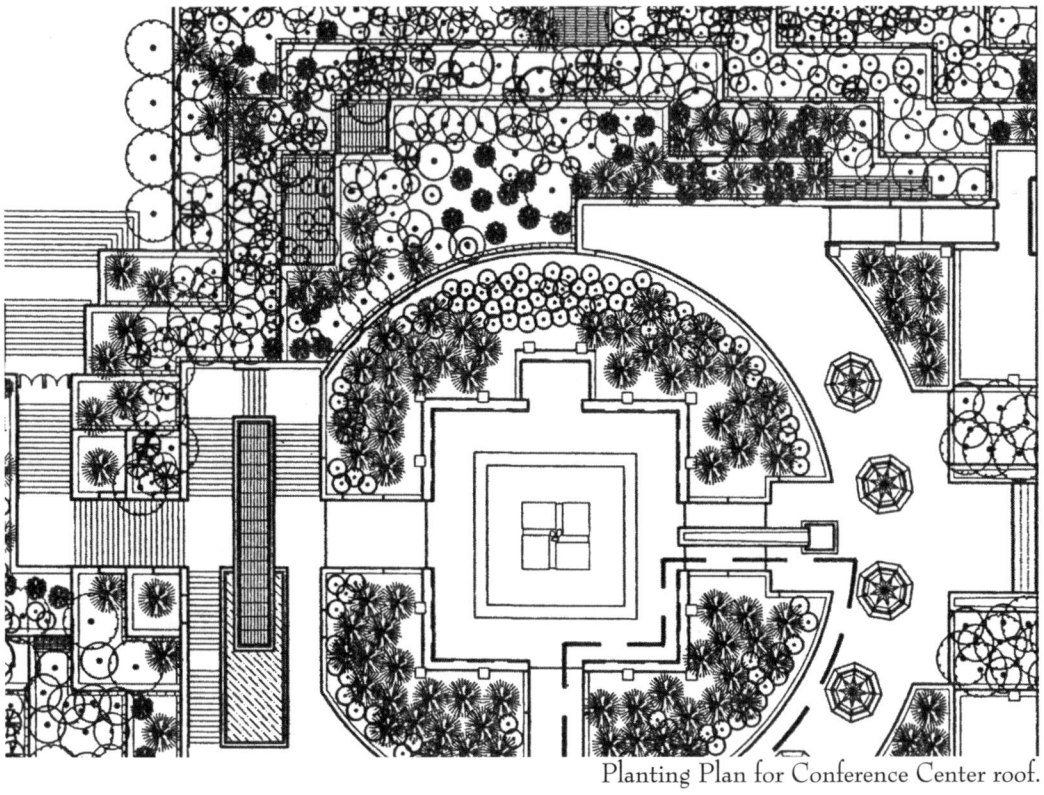
Planting Plan for Conference Center roof.

generated the move towards making it a multi-use hall.

"It dawned on us that today's modern theaters, like the Ordway in Minneapolis and the Wortham in Houston, have been built as twin theaters. A large one of perhaps 800 to 1000 seats and a small one of anywhere from 100 to 300. Twin theaters have some real flexibility for the community. You can have a major performance in the big theater, but you can still handle small community events in the small theater next door. We made the proposal to the President that we add a small theater, next door as a twin.

take a totally different set of criteria. The President said, 'Let's do it.' It seemed better to spend a little more money to improve the flexibility of the building than to have a building that is limited in its capacities. So that's what

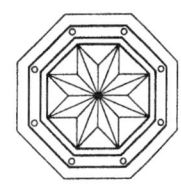

"The President's reaction in the beginning wasn't too enthusiastic. He said, 'Why do we need a theater?' One of his counselors very quickly responded and said, 'President, the first building Brigham Young built when he came into the valley was the Salt Lake Theater. The Saints need that culture in their lives.' The President wasn't disagreeing, but he was very concerned about budget. We did decide to add that building to the project and it has been a great blessing. It added an anchor to the west side of the building that was missing. It's given us some tremendous flexibility.

"If we had to do it all over again, we probably would do things a little differently. I would have asked the President for a little more time. One time Ted M Jacobsen said, 'President, could we maybe recognize the fact that the millennium starts in 2001, not 2000?' And the President smiled and said, 'Think 2000.' Well Ted pressed him a little more and said, 'President, could we maybe think October?' Do you know the President's response to that? The President said, 'At my age, I don't buy green bananas.'

"There was a point in time where the question was raised in the media that the President was pushing too hard, making the job cost more than it should and endangering lives, because he was pushing too hard. He wanted to make sure that wasn't true and we assured him it wasn't. Are we paying the premium for the schedule? We probably are to a degree, but who can predict what inflation is going to do. We haven't had the workers on a 24-hour shift yet, so I

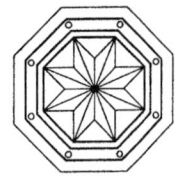

don't think it's been a totally unrealistic schedule."

Kerry Nielsen was hired as a project architect for The Church of Jesus Christ of Latter-day Saints in 1994. He received a degree in Engineering from Brigham Young University and a degree in Architecture from the University of Utah. He joined Leland Gray in working on the design and development of the Conference Center and continues as project architect. In reflecting on this significant project that he as a young architect participated in almost from its beginning stages, Nielsen gave this perspective on January 11, 2000:

"In January of 1995, Lee Gray and I went over to see President Hinckley. It was the first time we talked about this project, and by March of 1995 we had shifted our work load and activities and we were working pretty diligently doing a feasibility study. We had three private meetings with President Hinckley, and worked all that spring and through the summer, reporting to him in September of 1995 on our building studies, seating arrangements, and feasibility studies for the project.

"The need for this building was clear. People were standing in line all night to get into conference and couldn't get in. We started out with dealing with Preisdent Hinckley directly. He said, I'd like to see what you can do to get me 30,000 seats. Well after we listened intently and knew he wasn't joking, Lee and I went back on the boards and spent two or three months on the computer.

"I take pride in being able to deal with the whole

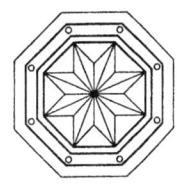

process and the big picture. I've had the incredible privilege of being there when we went through the beginnings. We started out designing a facility that could seat up to 30,000 people but we have always had two original requirements. It had to have good sight lines and seating position and it had to have excellent acoustics. So we went to work for two or three months trying to lay it out. A challenge was we weren't able to talk to anyone about this. As an architect, one of the first things I do is call on resources, consultants and specialists, but we were requested not to until we were told it was time.

"We presented some models and designs for a 30,000 seat scheme. It was almost impossible to fit it on the site, with its geometry, height, and profile. We took it in to the President and said that this is what it would take. We ended up doing some other site studies as a result of that. We had three sites that we considered putting this building on, but this one was always clearly the place.

"President Hinckley always knew when he wanted this facility ready. We never even thought about that at the beginning. We were concerned more with how we could design it appropriately to melt it into the neighborhood, the campus, the downtown district, the capitol historical district. The question was how can we set this building and still be sensitive to the surrounding environment and conditions. That's how we came up with building into the ground, the terrace, and lowering it down. We have got 65 feet of grade change around the site. West Temple and

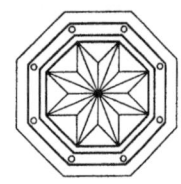

200 North is the low point and 200 North and Main Street is the high point, and it goes up another 30 feet.

"There will be people on Capitol Hill looking at the six acre roof of this building, so we designed a terrace, the roof top garden, with trees and meadows and so on. That idea came through inspiration, I'm sure. One day we were up on the hill trying to imagine what this building really needed to be in terms of the city scape. Two of our key consultants, Olin and Frasca, suggested that we have a finished landscape versus just a roof. That's the current design today.

"Lee Gray and I had been flying all around the country looking at facilities, touring auditoriums, arenas, theaters; we had been looking for the big building that was out there. We finally found Auditorium Nationale which is in Mexico City, which at the time was the closest thing to an auditorium. It was enclosed and indoor. It was still only 10,200 seats. Ours would be double the size. We came back and started the process with the design team.

"We brought in consultants at this point. The project was under way and we decided that to take this thing any further, we needed to develop a real team and get it going. This was prior to October Conference of 1995. We thought that maybe the President might say something about the project or announce it. He talked about it in a meeting with us, then chose not to. We worked hard all through the winter. We got some consultants going and some things in motion and had a scheme ready that we thought was achievable.

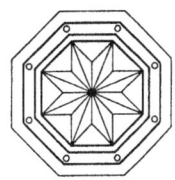

The project was announced in April of 1996.

"We started doing full blown presentations that next April, 1997. That's when the model was built and our ideas were presented to the First Presidency, the Twelve and the Presiding Bishopric. We were all holding our breath wondering how they would react to this model, and the roof gardens and trees on top. They received it very well. President Hinckley got up, started walking around and looked at the model and went to the end and leaned over and said, 'This is great, but Angel Moroni is not facing the right direction. And is this supposed to be centered on the temple? It's off center.'

"That really broke the ice and the concept was received very well. We brought the project to that point and made some recommendations. We were still doing studies on the number of seats, but we finally said that the building was too big at 26,000. Now would you settle for 20,000, President? And he said, 'I'd like to get at least 22,000 or as close as we can.' So that was our mark we said we could do it and make it work. We'll have 21,200 seats in the main hall. We're going to seat all the general authorities including the two full quorums of the seventy, plus a 350 seat choir, plus about 20,000 people in chair seats. The small theater has 905 additional seats.

"It was a long process. Our design work started in earnest in August 1996 and we had a work package out early in the spring. We closed the block at the end of May and we started demolition. We had the groundbreaking

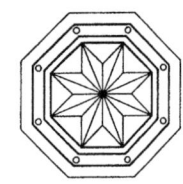

ceremony on the 24th of July, 1997. President Hinckley expected to have this building ready for April of 2000, and at that time it seemed like, oh, two years, no problem.

"I think we had 33 months if I remember right. It was an aggressive schedule. And now we're counting days. We have 71 working days to go. I believe we're going to do it. We're going to make it happen. We won't be air tight, done, but we'll be ready. There will be finishes still going on. We've had an incredible process with design.

"One of our goals, has been to convince people that we could do this, and now we're 71 working days away! Some of us may drop at the finish line. I was sitting here working at 11:30 last night and someone just asked me why I wasn't home. And I said, "We're asking these guys to knock themselves out. It's only fair that we're pulling our share too."

For the next two years a small group began to explore different engineering and architectural plans for a building that could accommodate 20,000 to 25,000 seats. During the course of their examination, the initial design team visited numerous sports arenas, national theaters and auditoriums throughout the world in order to get a feel for the construction techniques and methods needed to house such a large audience. After looking at structures ranging from the Pontiac Dome in Detroit to the 10,000-seat Auditorial Nationale in Mexico City, the planning group consulted with a team of renowned architects, structural engineers, acousticians and theatrical experts. Together they came up

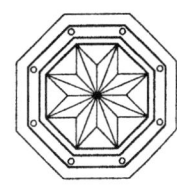

with a half dozen building schemes to present. One of the biggest dilemmas was President Hinckley's insistence that the main auditorium seat 21,000 people and that they have an unobstructed view of the speaker's pulpit! This meant that the structure was not only huge in its size and scope, but also void of an interior post supporting system.

Some of the initial design concepts were gigantic buildings ranging from 150 to 200-feet in height and encompassing more than a 10-acre area. These dimensions overpowered the site and everything surrounding it. This flew right in the face of President Hinckley's wishes to be sensitive to the nearby residents and also to the sacred and venerable buildings that were the "gems on Temple Square."

Another of the requirements for the Conference Center project was the need to design it to fit within the 75-foot height restriction so as to maintain the "permitted use" for the property as allowed by its existing zoning ordinance designation. Just how to accommodate such large-scale needs within a city block and not exceed the 75-foot "building envelope" was looking to be a mission impossible. Compared to the neighboring 26-floor Church Office Building with its 850,000 square feet of interior space, the new Conference Center would have 1,400,000 square feet.

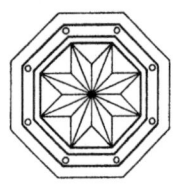

THE PROJECT IS ANNOUNCED

During the April 1996 sessions of LDS General Conference, President Gordon B. Hinckley twice mentioned the construction of a new meeting hall being considered by Church leaders.

"I am pleased to announce that we have had our architects and engineers working on the design of a hall which will seat three or four times as many for conference and which will serve other Church purposes as well as possibly some community cultural events," said President Hinckley during the Saturday morning session on April 6.

On Sunday morning April 7, 1996 President Hinckley said: "My heart reaches out to those who wish to get in [to general conference] and could not be accommodated. About a year ago I suggested to the Brethren that perhaps the time has come when we should study the feasibility of constructing another dedicated house of worship on a much larger scale that would accommodate three or four times the number who can be seated in this building. . . .

"The structure we envision will not be a sports arena. It will be a dedicated house of worship, and that will be its primary purpose. It will be fashioned in such a way that

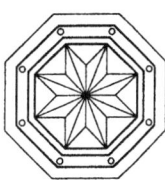

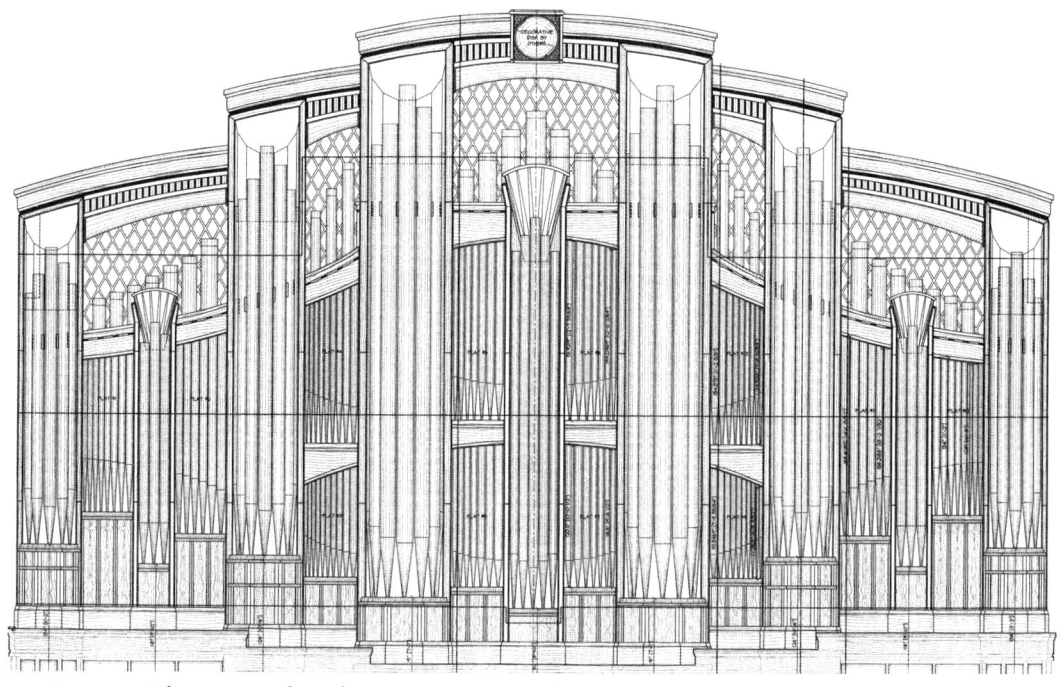
Rostrum Elevation with preliminary organ case design.

only a portion or the entire hall may be used, according to need. It will accommodate not only religious services, but will serve other Church purposes, such as the presentation of sacred pageants and things of that kind. It will also accommodate some community cultural events that will be in harmony with its purpose. The architectural and engineering studies have not gone far enough for us to make a detailed announcement, but the results thus far are encouraging." (*Ensign*, May 1996, 100.)

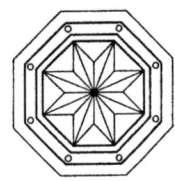

LEGACY CONSTRUCTORS

Thomas E. Hanson, Leland Gray, and Kerry Nielsen were members of the committee that selected the general contractor for the Conference Center. Nielsen gave the following insight into that final selection:

"This was a big project. We had national contractors pursuing this. Jacobsen, Okland, and Layton started out believing they could do this project themselves. They finally figured out they couldn't compete with the national contractors one at a time, so they got together and came back and said, "We'd like to do this project for you as a team." To keep everything fair in the process, we still finished the selection interviews. We had a hat, where we drew the order of the presentations. The Legacy team was last. From a presentation standpoint, you always want to be last. You always want to be the guy that gets the last shot at the selection committee. We had a selection committee of about eight people; Tom Hanson and I and Lee Gray and some others. We went through three days of two-hour presentations taking copious notes. It was pretty grueling. It was interesting to see the process; we were down to brass tacks now. We knew the project, we had a scope, we had a schedule, we had a budget. The Legacy

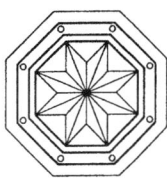

team selected Alan to give the closing statement for their presentation, and it swayed my vote.

"Projects of this scale, dollar volume, and schedule tend to get people very defensive and very self-centered. We've had a lot of open, bold and direct discussions. But you know, we're still talking to each other, we're still working together and we still have the interest of the project as the priority, and that's a great thing. Building can be a challenge and the stakes are high, so it's a credit to the Legacy team that they have maintained their perspective."

Alan S. Layton, a senior partner of Legacy Constructors and President of Layton Construction

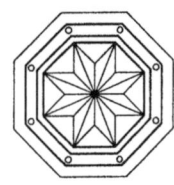

Company, Inc., made the following comments on December 9, 1999 about the formation of a very unique consortium of local contractors who won the bid to build the Conference Center:

"President Hinckley's announcement in 1996 generated a tremendous level of excitement in this wonderful project. Most of the local firms along with many large national constructors were all wondering and hoping to have some opportunity to be involved in the work. Initially, we were confident that Layton had both the capacity and the expertise for the project, and began internal planning and contacts with certain church building people.

"A little while later, when feeling disappointed after losing a big contract and thinking about the Assembly Building project, I felt a very strong impression that we needed to set aside our company pride and consider a joint venture with both the Jacobsen and Okland companies. The impression was direct yet very peaceful and I am so thankful for it. Contact was made to Randy Okland, whose firm was our partner with the Salt Lake County Adult Correction Facility and he told me that he and Ted Jacobsen had already talked about the benefits of teaming up. He arranged a meeting for the three of us to get together and talk about how such an organization could be set up and function. Out of that meeting came the Legacy joint venture.

"We are each 1/3 partners. Randy was selected to be the lead, and we have functioned much like a bishopric or presidency, Randy being the "Bishop". In fact, we have

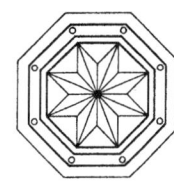

called him the Bishop. We have met every two weeks since that October day in 1996. We dealt with all manner of issues; the formation of the organization, the proposal and presentation to the Church people, negotiations of a reasonable and fair contract agreement, and for the past 27 months, the execution of the ideas and plans.

"This project has been a sobering stewardship. The trust and confidence of the First Presidency and other General Authorities and the Church building people has never been forgotten. We strive to be guided by the Spirit and always remember to make the correct decisions. The unity of our three-some has been wonderful. Never once in our meetings have we needed to take a vote. Our decisions have been made by consensus, much the same way a bishopric or presidency function. For me personally, this will be one of my most cherished memories of the project construction; the manner in which the three companies have worked together.

"This job has never been about how much money we could make. It's been about using our talents and our means and capability for the building up of the kingdom. That is very personal, but it's very much a part of our lives.

"The work has been difficult. We have had plenty of adversity and problems. But in spite of the difficulty, many little things have transpired that have been blessings helping to get the work completed. We started building well before the design had been completed. There were phases of the work that we could not proceed with because

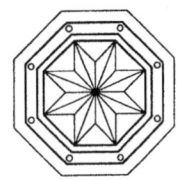

we had to wait for information and there were some things that we had to redo because the information was changing.

"We need to give a great deal of credit to our subcontractors. They have been heroic. I don't think any of them realized what they were getting into, but they have stuck with the immensity of their commitment and worked as was necessary. The building won't be 100% by April, but conference will occur and we hope President Hinckley will be pleased.

"There are three significant accomplishments that I believe need to be recorded; the personal sacrifice of the workmen and their families, the cooperation between the Church people and Legacy, and the miracle of the granite.

"Workmen like a little overtime. They can always use the extra money and it seldom really impacts their personal lives. In the case of the Assembly Building, the number of hours these men have worked has been almost unbelievable and the sacrifice the families have made has been huge. Vacations have been canceled. Ball games, music recitals, family outings and the like have mostly been forgotten. Yes, the additional money has been appreciated, but the family sacrifices have been far greater. These faithful workers, from the most skilled to the least, have recognized that this job was different; that this building was more about sacrifice of talent and time than it was about a paycheck.

"The teamwork and partnering between Tom Hanson and the Church people and Jim Peterson and the Legacy staff has been remarkable. Of course there have

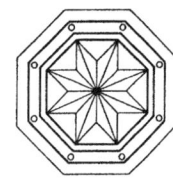

been times that emotions were strained and voices were raised, but feelings were always resolved and the work progressed. President Packer has taught that wonderful concept of being "equally yoked". On this project, we have felt yoked alongside the Church people and we believe that both parties have been pulling hard. Tom has been a marvelous statesman and Jim Peterson has been a strong leader who kept everyone's eye on the goal, and not the splinter in their finger or the rock in the shoe.

"It was from Harvey Wright that I first learned of the idea to use stone from Little Cottonwood Canyon, and immediately I sensed a special feeling about the idea. My wife, Leslie and I were present in June of 1998, when the Presiding Bishopric dedicated the quarry site and we felt the Spirit again. The use of this white stone compliments the Temple, and seems to speak that this building, too, is very special and sacred.

"I remember checking the sample panels that were prepared for the First Presidency's approval. The sunlight was casting upon the panels and the flecks in the stone glistened; almost iridescent in the light and I felt again that this was to be used on the building. I visited the quarrying operation several times during their work and marveled at the massive amount of work involved. I still look at the building and pause at the realization of what was required to build with Little Cottonwood granite."

J. Randy Okland of Legacy Constructors, commented in a similar vein on January 3, 2000:

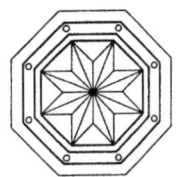

"When you're in construction and living in this valley and members of the Church, you're always very interested in those things which the Church is going to build. When we heard the announcement that the Church was going to build some type of a new assembly building, a large facility, we naturally wanted to be involved. We heard more about the project and we started to realize the magnitude of it, and we knew that it was something that we would like to do, but felt that there were some very good competitors.

Little Cottonwood Canyon granite. (Courtesy of W. Dee Halverson)

"We decided that we would approach the project as a joint venture with Layton and Jacobsen and I believe it was Alan Layton that came up with the name Legacy. I was designated to be the chairman of our group, and we formed a management coordination group of executives.

"One of the blessings that came about was the locating of Jim Peterson. His son, Alan Peterson, was working for Layton and we became aware of his experience working for The Austin Company in Seattle on the Boeing

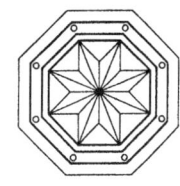

facilities. He had a great deal of experience on large span facilities and we knew this was going to be a large span facility. He had been with them for quite a few years and it was a great opportunity for us to have someone like that on our team. We brought him down and put him together with a lot of good people from every one of our companies and formed the organization.

"I don't think any one of us really realized the true magnitude of this project. As we started to get into our project meetings, the comment would often be made of how fortunate we were to get together with the group because of the magnitude, and the number of men that were required.

"There were times when each one of our firms had over 100 field people, not counting the management people in the office. In comparison to other projects that have been built in the valley and $100 million projects that we've built you might see a general contractor have maybe 100 men on the project at one time, but never 300 or 350 people doing just the concrete, besides the lead people. There was something that was guiding and directing all of us to get the group together. We have had a very cohesive group, and though we've debated a few things, we have all been uniform in our decisions and it's gone well.

"By the time the ground breaking occurred, we had our team together. Each company had decided who they were going to involve, and we keyed around using Jim as our pivot point, as our project executive on site. Jim has really been the man! There have been a lot of times that

we have gone to meetings and we were all a little bit pessimistic about meeting the dates, and the speed of this project. Jim has always been a very positive influence and no matter what the rest of us say, he keeps steering us in that direction. I have felt good about meeting the date. I've always felt good about it. I think it's going to happen.

"I've felt comfortable because of the people we have there, and the respect that the subcontractors have for the Church and their buildings. Nothing is perfect in this industry when you're working with thousands of people. We probably have 1,100 people up there right now. It's not going to be completely done, but it will be at a stage that they can hold a nice conference and the building can be completed and dedicated in October of 2000."

The third member of the group, Ted M. Jacobsen, senior partner of Legacy Constructors and Chairman of Jacobsen Construction Company, added the following insight on December 16, 1999:

"The Church had indicated that it was going to accept proposals from various contractors who were interested in serving as the construction manager on the Conference Center. Okland and Jacobsen were already working in a joint venture relationship on one or two projects and so Randy Okland and I had some discussions about proposing to the Church as the Jacobsen/Okland joint venture. We knew that we'd be competing against other local contractors, but we were more concerned about the fact that there would be some very large national contractors

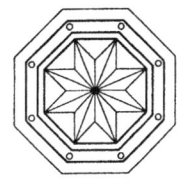

competing for the same contract. We felt that by combining we would have enough collective experience and expertise that we would be favorably compared to national competitors.

"Alan Layton contacted us and asked if he might be a part of the team and Randy and I considered it and met with Alan. It seemed to make good sense. It strengthened our ability to be successful. Normally our three companies are very fierce competitors, so it was like the lamb lying down with the lion.

"Most of the national companies who were interviewed for the project, teamed up with a local Salt Lake based company to give them local presence. We worked very cooperatively in putting together our proposal, prepared for the interview and selected the team that we were going to propose to the Church, who would be our project manager, who would be our construction manager on site and those kinds of things. At that point in time, there had not been much completed in terms of finalizing drawings. It's turned out to be a bigger project than we or the Church thought at the time we were making the proposal, yet the completion date has remained immovable, which has been a big challenge.

"At the time we proposed on the project we weren't sure of a finish date. It became crystal clear at the groundbreaking on July 24, 1997, when President Hinckley indicated that it would be open in April of 2000 for conference. That sort of clarified things in a hurry.

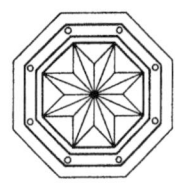

"Our marching orders were there and so we tried to figure out a way to get it done. It has gone very quickly. The architects and engineers were designing the building as fast as they could, and in some cases they couldn't review and coordinate their drawings as they would have under a normal situation, because of the time pressures. It's been a challenge for everyone on the design team, and the construction team, to move it along.

"The three partners have contributed some people to the project management team. Roughly a third of them are Jacobsen people, a third of them are Okland people and a third of them are Layton people. The project accountant has responsibility for the entire project, even though he's an Okland man. He's not just accounting for Okland, he's accounting for the entire project. The project safety director has responsibility for the entire project. Harvey Wright, who is the construction manager, even though he's a Jacobsen man, has responsibility for all of the field work that goes on. He divided the concrete work into areas of responsibility. Layton constructed the radial or the curved wall, during the concrete phase. Okland's principal responsibility was the underground parking structure, and Jacobsen had everything north and east of the radial wall. If a contractor had some challenges meeting its schedule or had some crews freed up, we moved them over onto the edges of another contractor's responsibility. It's been a very cooperative and supportive relationship."

Harvey E. Wright is Manager of Construction for

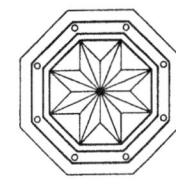

Legacy Constructors. He has been in the construction industry since 1948 and gave the following comments on January 11, 2000:

"Legacy consists of the three general contractors. Each company has stood on their own. They've had assignments, but if somebody got behind and we needed more assistance in an area, I was able to use some forces from one of the companies to pick up any slack.

"The parking structure and the outside work was done by Okland Construction with some incidentals inside. Layton Construction took the radius wall around, and the roof section. Jacobsen Construction had the buttresses on the north side and around the loading dock area, and all of the concrete work on the east and north side. Many of those walls were up to two feet thick and they're over 100 feet high. It's the biggest concrete job that I've ever witnessed being done.

"We've had up to 1,000 people working here and it's been a pleasure to work with these men and women. Everybody has their own way of doing things, but we plugged along. I worked the schedule and had a vision in mind. Every job has a number of ways that it can be worked out. Because of the location of this project, the staging of trucks was critical. We left a large hole in the radius wall in the northwest corner and brought the cranes out of there and dug the hole. It was my job every day to make sure we were getting our production, but also to have access. Everybody has to be able to have room to get their work

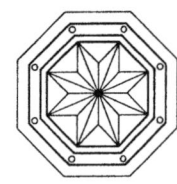

done, and I've had to watch that we don't shut them off. It's not easy to pull the trucks in and out without blocking and delaying someone's work."

James G. Peterson is Chief Executive of Legacy Constructors. During his 26-year career with The Austin Company, Jim was involved with large construction projects for the Boeing Company including the world's largest building by volume in Everett, Washington. About the Conference Center he commented on December 3, 1999:

"I have the task of supervising the complete project, including the accounting, purchasing, scheduling, and construction. The Legacy team is organized with about 30 people working for Legacy in each area, with two members from each of the companies that form what we call the partners. It is like a board of directors. I report to those six men. Randy Okland is the chairman of that group, Ben Nilsen from Okland, Alan Layton and George Ambrose from Layton are representatives, Ted Jacobsen and Lonnie Bullard are from Jacobsen. We report back to them in a meeting every two weeks and I'm responsible to operate the job. If we need some help from them, we ask, otherwise they leave us alone and we get it done. The relationship with these three companies has been excellent. They're all very strongly behind this project, and give us whatever support we need. We've had minimal problems.

"This project has unique features and very high quality finishes. Probably the biggest challenge has been the schedule because the design development and

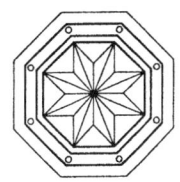

engineering was going on during construction. We've worked in phases on the project as the design has been completed. Legacy has done an excellent job by adapting to the requirements of the schedule, and we've got about fifty very good sub-contractors on the job and a good team of workers to make it happen.

"At the peak of the project we had about 1,100 workers. We broke ground and started the demolition in June of 1997. We cleared the site of the old Deseret Gym, the parking lot, and Mormon Handicraft building. Then the excavation and the shoring started. At that time our team was small, but we built up from that time until the fall of 1999. From now on we'll be reducing our personell. These crews gave us a very strong and stable work force."

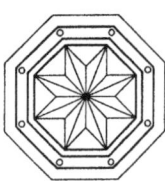

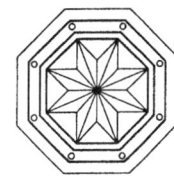

PRAYER AT GROUNDBREAKING

by President Gordon B. Hinckley

"Now if you will close your eyes and bow your heads, we'll join in a brief prayer of dedication as we break ground this July 24, 1997:

"Oh, God our Eternal Father. We bow before thee this historic day with gratitude and thanksgiving in our hearts. We're thankful for the purpose for which we've met. We feel under thy divine inspiration and direction and guidance and under the spirit of inspiration and revelation we have concluded to go forward with the construction of a great new assembly hall here to house thy people, that they may worship together in large numbers and enjoy other undertakings beneath its great roof. We thank thee for all who are assisting to make it possible. We thank thee for the faith of the Saints everywhere who have contributed of their tithes and offerings, which make possible this great undertaking.

"Now, we pray for thy blessings upon it as we go forward. We break the earth this day as our forebearers first broke the earth with their plows in this valley 150 years ago. We commence this construction undertaking and pray for thy blessings. May it go forward, may none be injured. May there be no serious accidents of any kind. May the

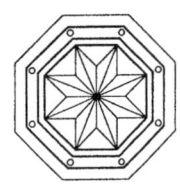

work move at a pace to it's completion and may it be, when it's all finished a thing fitly framed together, everything working in harmony, one with another, the sound, the lighting, the acoustics, everything which means so much in the construction of a building of this kind. And when it is all done, may we again appear before thee with thankful hearts and gratitude unto thee for thy blessings upon us for bringing it to pass.

"Please accept of our thanks. Please assist us in that which we undertake to do. Please hear and answer our prayers. Please smile with favor upon us we humbly ask in the name of Him whom we love and in whose name we meet to carry forward thy great work, even the Lord Jesus Christ, Amen."

President Gordon B. Hinckley in a hard hat. (Courtesy of Gary Holland)

September 29, 1997.

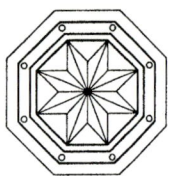

1997

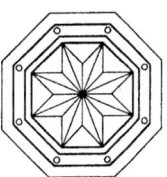

September 29, 1997.

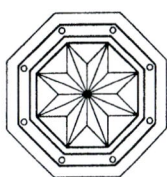

September 29, 1997.

October 30, 1997.

January 21, 1998.

January 21, 1998.

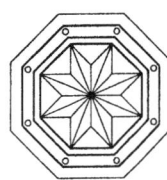

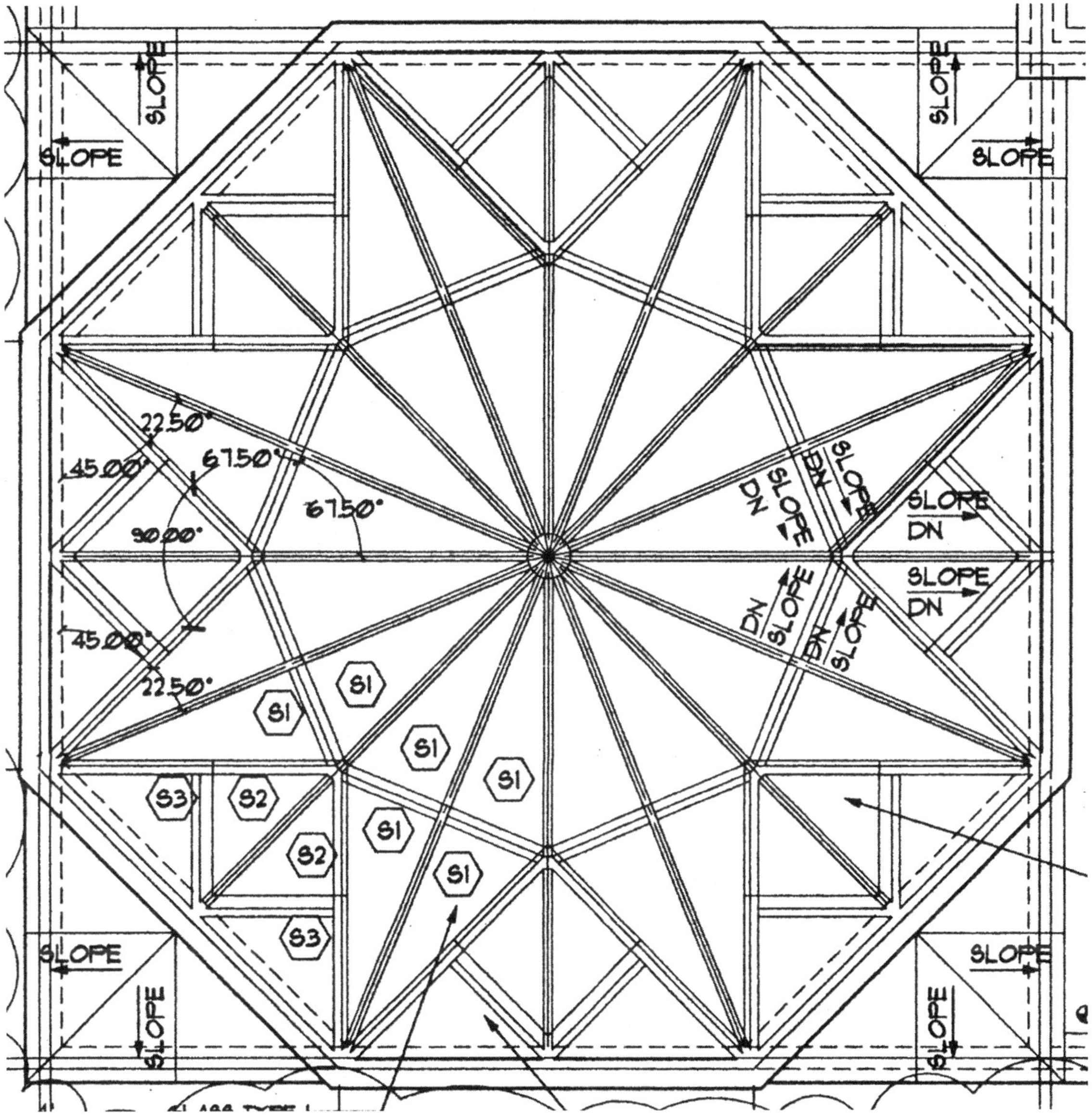

Lobby skylight--plan view of exterior details.

CHAPTER TWO

1998

MIRACLE IN PROGRESS

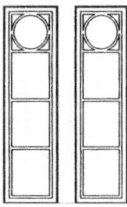

One of the biggest hurdles for the construction of the Conference Center during 1998 was securing the final permits for the extraction of the granite for the project from the Church-owned property in Little Cottonwood Canyon. The following Deseret News article appeared on May 20, 1998: "LDS Church Gets OK To Quarry Its Granite. After weeks of controversy, the LDS Church was given official permission Wednesday to retrieve granite from Little Cottonwood Canyon. The granite, taken from the same site as the stone used to build the Salt Lake LDS Temple a century ago, will be cut into slabs to face the church's large new assembly hall, now being constructed. After the unanimous decision by the Salt Lake County Commission, church officials expressed relief— anxious to get going.

"The permit will allow The Church of Jesus Christ of Latter-day Saints two years to complete its granite

FACTS & STATS

- King Truss is 152 feet long and weighs 621 tons.
- 10 radial trusses are 230-287 feet long.
- Estimated 116,00 total cubic yards of concrete.
- 15,000 tons of concrete reinforcing steel (#18 rebar).
- 12,000 tons of structural and miscellaneous steel.
- Perimeter concrete walls and interior shear wall up to 30 inches thick.
- Little Cottonwood granite used in 1 1/2" thick panels on west and south facing walls, while east and north wall faced with granite ashlar (rough surfaced stone of random lengths laid in a brick pattern). Approximately 300,000 square feet total.

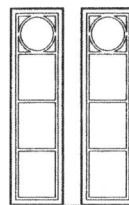

retrieval operations and an additional year to mitigate the damage by installing top soil and planting vegetation. One opponent maintained that the church should be required to replace the boulders as well, but that argument didn't get very far. Opponents had argued that the operation would destabilize the mountainside, endanger people living and driving beneath the operation and cause long-term esthetic damage to the area, which is frequented by rock climbers and others.

"The general feeling of the county and planning commissioners was that in the past the church has tried hard to accommodate rock climbing and other recreational uses of its property, even though it didn't have to, and that it should now be allowed to make use of it in a way that was not overly destructive. . . ."

In her two-part series *A Conversation With LDS President Gordon B. Hinckley*, KSL-Television's religion specialist, Carole Mikita, touched on the relationship between Mormons and non-Mormons in Salt Lake City: "The building of the new center has not always been smooth sailing for the LDS Church. President Hinckley told me it's time to put all of that aside and let the community know 'all are welcome here.' The new Conference Center was designed specifically not to overshadow, but to compliment the Salt Lake Temple. Facing on the walls is the same granite that was used to build the temple. It came from Little Cottonwood Canyon, but this time there were residents who complained that excavating the stone was

noisy, dusty and dangerous for them. President Hinckley says he's sorry."

"There's been a little friction and a little trouble," said President Hinckley. "To anybody who has been discommoded, we give our apology. But we are grateful that it's worked out the way it has and we hope that no one has been injured in the result.

"I regret any animosity perceived or real that might occur. I don't like it, I don't think it is needed. I don't think it's necessary and I don't think it's warranted.

"We hope that [the Conference Center] will serve a great community purpose, as well. . . and that people from all over this area, members of the Church and non-members will feel welcome to come there, enter it and look upon it and feel of the spirit there and enjoy it." (Utah News from KSL-TV, February 28, 2000)

The following tongue-in-cheek newspaper article appeared in the Salt Lake Tribune, on November 29, 1999 under this headline: "Divine Intervention? When LDS Church officials requested a permit from Salt Lake County to remove granite from the church quarry in Little Cottonwood Canyon for the new assembly hall, commissioners gave their OK with this condition: No granite could be removed from the canyon once the ski season had started. Contractors finished extracting the granite last week— the week the resorts were graced with snow."

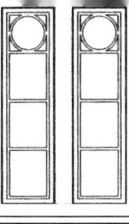

Little Cottonwood Canyon boulder field. (Courtesy of Dallas Orchard)

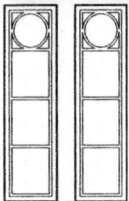

ROCK OF AGES

Leland Gray, one of the Church architects that worked closely with President Hinckley during the early planning stages of the Conference Center, made the following comments about the decision to use granite from the Little Cottonwood Canyon on January 6, 2000:

"At the very beginning of the Conference Center project, President Hinckley indicated his feelings about facing the building with the same granite that had been used on the Salt Lake Temple. So we followed up on his suggestion to investigate the availability of Little Cottonwood Canyon granite stone.

"On the north side of the road up Little Cottonwood Canyon, about a third of a mile further east, hidden by the trees, you can see the cliff with the vaults at the bottom. In between the two the granite boulders have fallen off the top of the cliff and tumbled down into the gulch. Some of these boulders weighed up to 600 tons. They're monstrous. They're bigger than houses. When the early Mormon pioneers did their quarrying, they were down by the creek and a little further down the canyon. The boulders were brought from the top of the canyon down by the glacier.

"The stone has an incredible legacy to it. Every

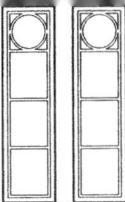

Harvesting granite for the Salt Lake Temple. (Courtesy of Utah State Historical Society)

time I go to that quarry site, it's really a boulder field, I sense a feeling and a spirit there that defies common understanding. I feel like somebody else made the decision that we were going to use that stone a long time ago. We have had two workers from Mexico up at the quarry who have been baptized into the LDS Church as a result of working there, and one at the plant up in Idaho Falls. You get touched deeply by this stuff.

"The stone comes with inclusions, those dark spots that you see and streaks of quartz and other imperfections

in the stone that to most people would be objectionable. During one visit to the building site I said, 'President Hinckley, how do you feel about these inclusions?'. He got a big smile on his face and said, 'Aren't they beautiful?'"

As the discussion went back and forth regarding the final selection of the stone that would be used on the exterior of the new Conference Center, Alan S. Layton related this personal and first hand insight on December 9, 1999:

"During the discussions about using the Little Cottonwood Canyon granite, I remember that there were some mock ups made. There were stones from several quarries around the country that were produced by commercial, established stone companies. There was also a sample of the Little Cottonwood granite laying there, and I remember looking at it. There is a sparkle in that stone when the sunlight is just right on it, and the way this sample had been set up on the site, the way it was facing the sun, the stone had almost an iridescent appearance to it. It was far whiter than the material that had been brought in from the commercial sources out of state. There was a sparkle to it that I can't describe. The First Presidency was coming over a day or two later to look at the different samples, but I walked away and told my wife that it would be Little Cottonwood stone, no question. It almost had a radiance about it. The coloration and the iridescence or

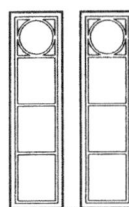

whiteness that was there gave it a very special appearance.

"We have that very special connection to the Salt Lake Temple and all it stands for. The gospel will be taught and understood within the new Conference Center and lives will be changed and forever blessed by virtue of the experiences that the people will have there. The sacred nature of the building will allow the Church to conduct business there that would not otherwise be possible."

Theodore R. "Ted" Orchard and his company, Idaho Travertine, played a significant role in the discovery, extraction and processing of the huge amount of granite stone used to cover the massive Conference Center. The total quantity of Temple Granite used on the building, nearly

The first method of transporting granite.
(Courtesy of Utah State Historical Society)

300,000 square feet, was the equivalent of a football field-sized area piled 10-feet high with solid stone. Here is his account of the "miracle of the stone" given on March 9, 2000:

"In July, 1997 I was asked by The Church of Jesus Christ of Latter-day Saints to give an opinion on the availability of granite on Church property in Little Cottonwood Canyon. I was to determine if there was stone of sufficient quantity and quality to clad the LDS Assembly Building (later named the Conference Center). This granite was the same stone used on the Salt Lake Temple.

"Church architect Leland Gray, my son Cliff and I went to Little Cottonwood Canyon and evaluated the available stone on the Church's property, which includes the mountain side from the storage vaults up the canyon approximately one mile and most of the land north of Highway 210. After several hours of climbing the mountain side, we discovered an area which we felt contained enough stone of adequate quality to provide the required amount for this project. I felt we were led and inspired by the Holy Ghost in actions and determinations that day!

"I have been told that representatives of other firms visited the site and determined that it was not feasible to obtain the stone from that area in sufficient quantities and quality to provide finished stone for the Conference Center project.

"Subsequent to the visit to the Little Cottonwood Canyon property, I was asked to determine if Idaho

Travertine Corporation (owned by my wife and myself) would be interested in quarrying and fabricating (slabbing, cutting and finishing) the stone required for the project from the Little Cottonwood granite. After several days of family consultation, fasting and prayer with sons Tim, Cliff and Bill, we determined that with help from the Lord we would be able to accomplish that which was asked of us.

"Idaho Travertine Corporation is a family business which prior to this job, quarried and fabricated dimensioned stone of a softer variety, such as travertine, limestone, marble and sandstone. Although ITC has for years purchased granite slabs from other firms and fabricated them for residential and small commercial jobs, this project was our first experience with quarrying and fabricating blocks of granite. ITC has furnished our Continental Buff Travertine in larger quantities than this project. Our largest job to date was a 650,000 sq. ft. project for the Southwest Bell Telephone complex in Dallas, Texas.

"During the Fall of 1997 ITC did a considerable amount of research to determine the best equipment for the job ahead. In February, 1998 we were issued a purchase order from the LDS Church to quarry and fabricate the Little Cottonwood granite and we immediately began buying some required equipment, which we did not already have.

"For several years my brother, Dallas Orchard, has worked for ITC intermittently in differing capacities. Dallas' schedule developed in such a way that he and his

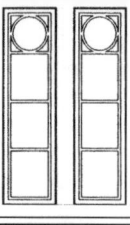

Idaho Travertine workers using modern techniques and equipment on Little Cottonwood granite. (Courtesy of Dallas Orchard)

family were available and able to move to Sandy, Utah and live in a house that ITC leased near the quarry site. Dallas agreed to be the quarry supervisor and his wife, Charlotte, has been very adept at scheduling trucks to haul the blocks from the quarry.

"When the decision was made to use the granite from Little Cottonwood Canyon, several individuals in the Salt Lake area objected to the perceived environmental impact on the quarry site. Some of them challenged the right of Salt Lake County to issue permits to the LDS Church to extract stone from the site. As a result of these legal challenges and the desire of the Church to be environmentally responsible, twenty-one limiting restrictions were placed on the quarrying process

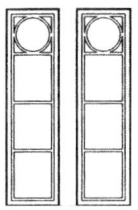

and a three month delay was imposed. ITC was granted permission to enter the quarry site on May 28, 1998. After the permit was granted there have been other attempts through the courts to stop the quarrying. The LDS Church personnel and legal department have skillfully handled all these legal challenges which allowed ITC to continue.

"ITC was able to quarry enough granite blocks prior to the winter closure of the quarry to keep their saws busy right through to the Spring of 1999, when the quarrying was resumed in March, 1999. In April, 1998 the decision was made to substitute split-faced granite on much of the east and north elevations of the Conference Center instead of smooth granite panels as originally designed. This decision resulted in ITC purchasing additional diamond-wire saws and a stone splitter. Because this split-faced stone could be fabricated from smaller quarried pieces, ITC leased a building in Salt Lake City and installed the two wire saws and a splitter at that location. This leased facility resulted in substantial savings in freight costs. Cliff Orchard moved to Salt Lake City to manage this part of the operation. After most of the split-faced stone was fabricated, a coping saw was added to the Salt Lake plant so that some of the cubic stone could also be produced there.

"In the Spring of 1999 the decision was made to use granite stone fabricated in Minnesota for stair treads, pavers, and fountains. The total amount of Little Cottonwood Canyon granite required was 280,000 feet of dimensional stone-panels and cubic stones). More than

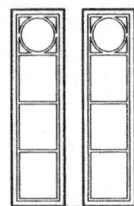

2,900 different-sized pieces with multiples of each size for a total of 34,000 pieces were required to finish the Conference Center project.

"In addition to the complex job of fabricating stone in the required sequence for installation, the scheduling was very critical. Tim Orchard has handled the correlation of fabrication and shipping to the job site, as well as many other administrative duties. Bill Orchard has had the responsibility of supervising the fabrication and meeting shipping deadlines at the Idaho Falls plant. Keith Johnson has supervised the slabbing and specialty-piece sawing. All of these are very demanding. Both the Idaho and Salt Lake plants have operated 24-hours per day, 6 days per week to meet the schedule.

"To facilitate the scheduling and tracking of the thousands of stone pieces, Frank Anderson was hired to work part time supervising quality control and computer programing. This has been a very great help. The opportunity to work with people, such as the Legacy Constructors, B & T Masonry, Caffall Tile, ZGF architects and the LDS Church personnel has been a very positive experience. We at ITC greatly appreciate the association with all these fine people. Although the schedule and demands for a very high quality job in a very short time frame were at times stressful, all went well.

"To the Orchard family, as well as many others involved in the stone quarrying and fabrication process, the participation in the construction of the LDS Conference

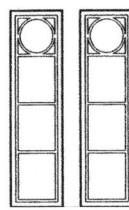

Center has been a spiritual experience which will be long remembered after the physical and mental stresses have been forgotten. Because the complexities of this undertaking strained our resources and abilities, we relied greatly on receiving inspiration and help from the Lord. As a result many miracles were witnessed in all phases of this project. We are grateful to have had a part in building this historic structure."

Dallas Orchard, Ted's brother, was responsible for the on site extraction of the massive granite stones from Little Cottonwood Canyon in Salt Lake City and their transportation to the processing facilities of Idaho Travertine in Idaho Falls. The day-to-day operations of this tremendous effort were filled with both daunting challenges and faith-promoting experiences. Here in his own words Dallas describes both:

"I was contacted by my brother, Ted Orchard in the late Fall of 1997 and was asked if I would help in the extraction of granite out of Little Cottonwood Canyon. At that time I was installing granite for Ted in Sun Valley, Idaho plus helping my wife, Charlotte, run a restaurant in Carey, Idaho. I told Ted that I would let him know after talking it over with Charlotte.

"After prayerful consideration, we both agreed that we would help in the Conference Center project, so I let Ted know that I would go to Salt Lake City. Not long after that he told me that he had been informed that he and his company would not be involved in the job. We were

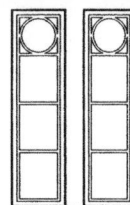

quite surprised because we had all felt that we should be involved.

"I enrolled in school in order to get my real estate licence and also made an offer to buy a ranch in the Carey, Idaho area. Sometime around the middle of February 1998 Ted let me know that things had changed and that we had been issued a purchase order from the Church to furnish granite for the Conference Center. The Lord took care of us as we made arrangements to move down to Salt Lake, put our plans in Carey on hold and found a place to lease for two years. On April 1, 1998 Charlotte and I with our children Nathan (16) and LaToya (14) moved to Salt Lake.

"We weren't able to actually begin the extraction of granite until the 28th of May, because of the legal action taken against the Church for its plans to use granite from the Little Cottonwood Canyon area. After we received all of the necessary permits the first thing we had to do was to remove the trees and brush in order to build a road to the area from which we intended to extract the stone. We started shipping rock to our plant in Idaho Falls, Idaho for processing during the first part of June 1998.

"I had Keith Johnson come down to help run the equipment. We hired Nathan Peterson, a returned missionary from Portugal who was able to speak fluent Spanish. This became a great asset to us because most of

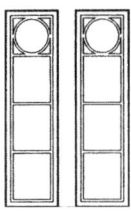

the men working on the site were Mexican. We hired Bill Calloway to help us with the drilling process. In the Spring of 1999 Theo Orchard, Ted's oldest son, took a leave of absence from his job with Orem City to help us with the physical removal and transportation of stone from the site. He was a great help in all aspects of the work.

"From the first time I saw the project, I felt a strong need that the quarry site should be dedicated. I discussed my feelings with Bishop Keith B. McMullin during one of his visits to the site. On June 12, 1998 the Presiding Bishopric of the Church came to the quarry with others involved with the project. Bishop H. David Burton dedicated the site and blessed it to be a safe work place and that the knowledge to extract the rock would come to those running the project.

"We completed the extraction of the granite stone on December 18, 1999. There were no days lost-time accidents during the entire time. The worst injury was suffered by Bill Cook who lost the end of his ring-finger tip while loading a truck. Because of the very steep grade in part of the quarry area, the danger of accident to men and equipment was ever present. The primary danger was a slide area where large granite boulders had piled on top of each other. Quarrying these stones was similar to playing *Pick Up Sticks*, except we were working with rocks that weighed up to 600 tons.

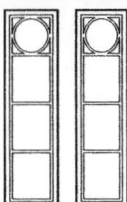

Little Cottonwood Canyon boulder field. (Courtesy of Dallas Orchard)

"The work schedule was determined by the daylight hours available and consisted mostly of ten to twelve hour shifts, six days a week. Many times after a day's work, we would return the next morning to find boulders, which had slid down during the night, laying in position to be drilled and split.

"In extracting the rock our main effort was to get stones out that could be cut into slabs measuring 4 feet x 8

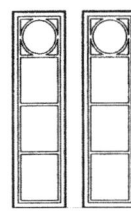

feet x 1-1/2 inches. The ideal rock to work with weighed about 28,000 lbs. The process we used was first to mark across the rock 54" and then drill the holes 8"-12" on center in a straight line to within a foot or two of its base. Next we would put one strand of 50-grain primer cord in each hole and connect these with a piece of 25-grain primer cord. We would then fill the holes with a product that controlled the power of the of the explosion, so that most of the force went from hole to hole. In that way we would get a slab of the edge of the boulder at least 54" thick. After tipping the slab over we would then mark it into pieces roughly 4' x 8' in size. We would then drill and split the block.

"Any rock between 10,000 and 40,000 lbs. was not split in the field, but sent directly for processing. We tried to send the rocks with straight edges to Idaho and the odd-shaped stones were sent to our Salt Lake processing plant, where they were given the desired rough-face finish and cut into pieces to be used on the east and north elevations of the Conference Center.

"Once the rock was split to size, we would remove it to the quarry road with the excavator, then pick it up with a track loader and take it down the hill to the loading area. We weighed each piece and wrote the weight on the rock for transportation. We matched up the stones to make up truck loads weighing from 45,000 to 52,000 pounds. Charlotte then would schedule various trucking companies to haul the stones to Idaho or to the Salt Lake plant.

"I will give you an idea of the amount of granite

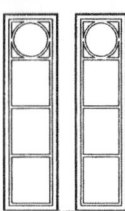

Salt Lake Temple construction, ca. 1870s. (Courtesy of Utah State Historical Society)

needed to complete the Conference Center. It would be the equivalent of filling a football field (300' long and 150' wide) to a depth of 10 feet of solid rock. In order to remove this enormous amount of material we hired up to 22 men to work full time during each of the harvesting seasons.

"I would like to thank all those who helped to complete the removal of the granite from the quarry site; the quarry workers, equipment maintenance people and suppliers who expedited repairs and deliveries. Also I want to acknowledge the many truckers who were willing to haul more than 1,400 loads of granite in all kinds of weather. Most of all I want to thank the Lord that I could be involved in this project and for providing a safe work place and inspiration to complete the work."

THE "KING TRUSS" STEEL ROOF SUPPORT SYSTEM

The unique design and construction challenges of the Conference Center were featured in a *Civil Engineering* magazine article that appeared in January 2000. "Designers had to balance the seemingly conflicting goals of providing a large audience capacity and creating the ambience of an intimate gathering. The solution was to submerge a large portion of the building deep beneath the surface and to landscape the roof by creating a series of terraces that would conform to the sloping site and reflect the surrounding landscape.

"The preliminary structural design of the complex began in the fall of 1996 by addressing the two greatest challenges: designing a building partially embedded up to 90 feet below grade and creating a 21,000-seat, column-free assembly space. The unobstructed views from every corner that the Church wanted required long-span roof trusses— up to 290 feet— designed for loads between 250 and 525 pounds per square foot to account for the rooftop landscaping.

"Although the new conference center was designed

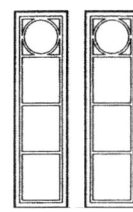

in accordance with the 1994 Uniform Building Code, which categorizes Salt Lake City as seismic zone 3, the Church wanted the structure to last at least 150 years. That meant that the structure had to be designed to withstand seismic forces far greater than those addressed by the code."

Nathan Charlton, one of the authors of the article, was the project engineer representing KPFF Consulting Engineers of Portland, Oregon for the Conference Center. On December 30, 1999 Mr. Charlton related his personal feelings about the building's unique engineering design:

"This is a magnificent project. Fortunately, KPFF has done a lot of long-span truss design. When we heard about a building with truss spans of 290 feet, while that's quite impressive, it was something that we're very comfortable in designing. When we found out that the roof of the structure would support a landscaped garden environment, with loads as high as 550 pounds per square foot, then the challenge became very exciting. That is something we do not do a lot of.

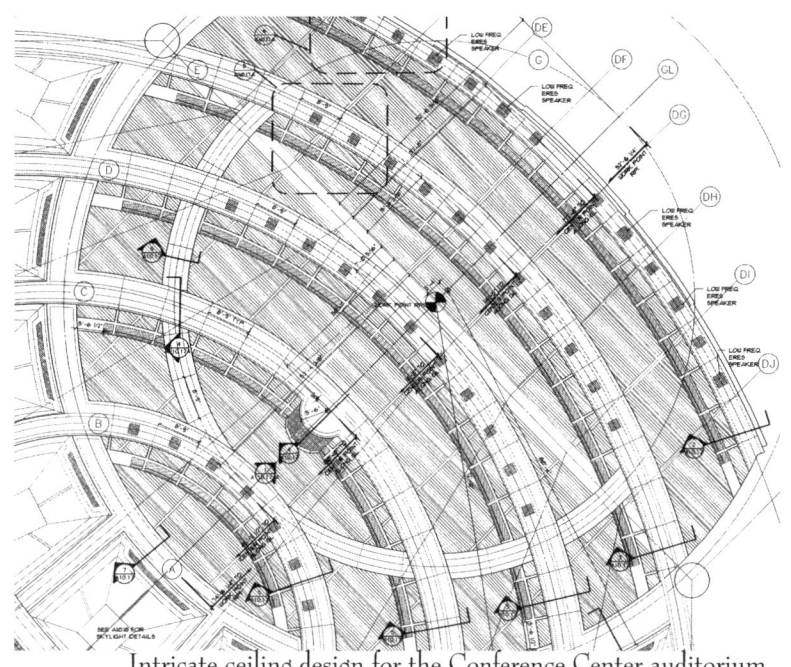

Intricate ceiling design for the Conference Center auditorium.

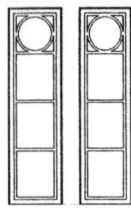

"We started talking with the project architect, Zimmer Gunsul Frasca, about the project in October of 1996. In the early phases of programming and design conception, there were ideas of incorporating pathways, ramps, and steps leading up to the garden roof. Endeavoring to support a rooftop landscape environment with long-span trusses presented us with many unique challenges.

"To provide column-free space below, we ended up with ten radial trusses and a transfer truss over the stage. A more conventional orthogonal truss configuration was considered, which would have resulted in many trusses of different lengths and geometric configurations. With the radial scheme, we ended up with ten trusses, five on either side of the center line of the building. These were, in fact, five pairs of trusses with each pair having similar geometry matching the required roof slope and bottom chord slope as a function of the interior hall sight lines.

"The radial truss scheme appeared to result in some fabrication economy because of the geometric similarities. The loading, however, varied in the trusses because of the configuration of the rooftop landscape. The notion of the king truss came about when we evaluated whether increasing the length of the trusses to the back wall of the house, supporting on the concrete structure, or using shorter roof trusses and a transfer truss would be more cost-effective.

"Given the short design schedule and the need for a steel mill order set of drawings for the procurement of roof

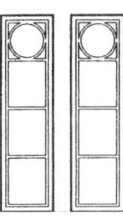

Conference Center "King Truss".

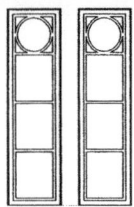

truss steel, the design team needed to make some very quick decisions about how many trusses could most cost-effectively support the roof given various span options. The structural steel fabricator and erector, Schuff Steel, provided valuable input in the decision making process regarding the availability of various grades of steel for the long-span trusses.

"The fact that the building was "pushed" into the ground, meant that we had to deal with very large soil static and dynamic (earthquake) pressures. The deepest excavation is about ninety feet to the bottom of the footings at the area behind the stage. This was a very significant excavation and kpff designed the excavation shoring for the entire project using a fairly common soldier pile-wood lagging tied back shoring system. An excavation of ninety feet in the ground is not something that is done everyday. On the south and east sides of the property, the excavation shoring is on the property line. The building volume extends all the way to the property line on these two sides. The fact that the excavation for this building varied between forty and ninety feet in depth precluded the use of conventional retaining walls to resist the soil pressures. The very large volume of the main hall extends to the perimeter building walls on the east and north sides. These walls are known as the east and north house walls bound by a 700 foot curved "radiused" wall at the back of the house.

"In multi-story buildings, typically floor plates brace exterior retaining walls. This is not the case in the

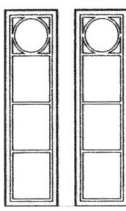

Conference Center with the very large volume spaces below cascading planters on the east and north sides above the First Presidency suites, mechanical space, and loading dock space. The design solution developed to resist soil loads as a result of the very deep excavation and large volume spaces was to incorporate buttress walls turned to the inside of the building at approximately thirty feet on center. These walls could not extend to the outside of the building because of the proximity of the property line. The buttress walls are 24 inches thick, and extend thirty feet into the building volume. The perimeter foundation walls span horizontally to the large buttresses. Very large foundations were required to resist the overturning forces from the soil pressure on the buttress walls. The buttress walls create cubbyholes every thirty feet that are used for First Presidency suites, mechanical spaces, and storage of rostrum components.

"The Uniform Building Code (UBC) dictates that Salt Lake City is in seismic zone three. The owner asked that we design the Conference Center based on the requirements for zone four, and also include an importance factor of 1.25. So in essence, the seismic loads induced into the structure by design are about 67% higher than they would be if we had followed the UBC zone three code requirements. Resisting the dynamic soil pressures provided to us by the geotechnical engineer, as a result of this enhanced code design, presented a formidable challenge and the buttress walls on the east and north sides worked very well in resisting these soil pressures.

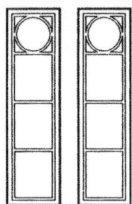

"There were some unique and challenging design elements of this building from a structural engineering standpoint. The roof long-span truss design was certainly quite challenging. The building foundation design for a building buried ninety feet in the ground, resisting enormous external soil pressures, was also very challenging. The design of the balcony seating area, cantilevering as much as 110 feet off the curving house wall, presented one of the most unique and challenging engineering design tasks. The owner's program requirements dictated that the entire 21,000 seat hall be column-free to avoid any obscured views of the stage, and to also create as intimate a space as possible. The balcony supports approximately 7,500 seats and is entirely column-free. To support the cantilevered balcony structure, the four large mechanical shafts on the lobby side of the curving house wall were incorporated into the design. Secondly, the floor areas (diaphragms) outside the curving house wall in the lobby areas play an integral role in the structural support of the

The "King Truss".

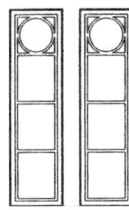

balcony system. The structural design task of the balcony support system was complicated by the number of penetrations made through the lobby floor for elevators, escalators, mechanical penetrations, etc. The balcony and mechanical mezzanine floor levels are heavily reinforced to resist the extraordinary cantilevered balcony forces. This was a fabulous project."

Some of the key elements of the structural steel truss system for the new Conference Center made an 8,000-mile journey. These double-wide-flange rolled sections of specialized steel are only available from the Arbed Steel plant in Belgium— this meant that their fabrication had to be carefully scheduled well in advance. Their delivery to Utah to meet with the other truss components involved a trans-Atlantic voyage from Rotterdam to the Panama Canal— then a voyage to San Francisco— then an overland railroad trip to the Mountain States Steel facilities in Lindon, Utah. There the King Truss and radial roof trusses were preassembled, then disassembled and sent on to the Salt Lake City for onsite assembly. All of the joints were bolted connections to avoid time-consuming welding in the field.

Blake Dallin, a Utah native and 30-year career man with The Austin Company, was hired out of retirement by the Legacy Constructors as the superintendent for structural steel construction. On February 23, 2000 Mr. Dallin gave a personal account of his perspective on this highly unique design and construction story:

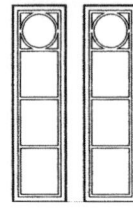

"The auditorium inside the Conference Center is unique in that it is a fan shape and everyone has a good view. There are no columns to obstruct any view. There are three levels of seating. At the upper level there is a balcony, which is a steel cantilever structure clad with concrete, pre cast concrete sections and supporting base. That cantilever's out 80 feet into the open space. In order to construct the building the way the engineers designed it, we had to place the balcony truss and prop it up with temporary columns. These columns were 16 inch diameter steel pipe, and they were probably 70 to 80 feet deep, where they were buried. Then the balcony had to be completed. The radius wall, which is the back wall of the house, and the structure behind that became a very large strong box, which actually gripped the end of this cantilever truss and allowed it to work and to carry a load of probably in the neighborhood of 6,000 plus people.

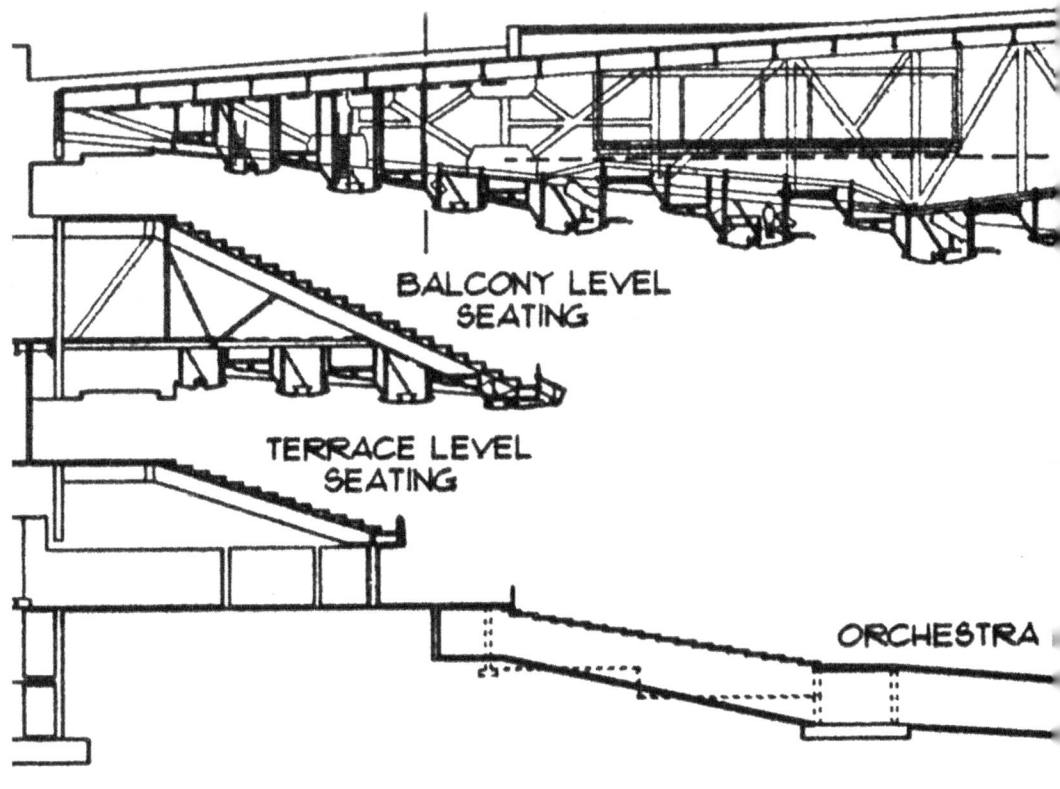

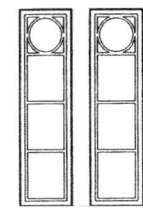

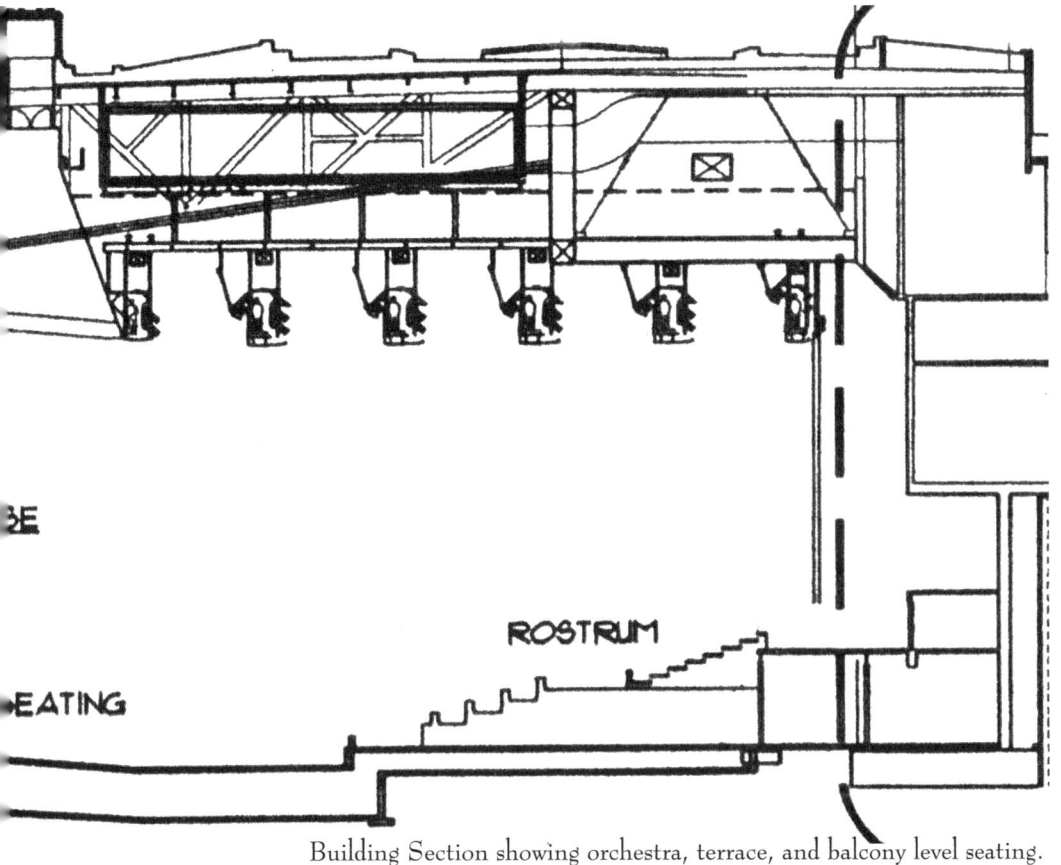
Building Section showing orchestra, terrace, and balcony level seating.

concrete that extend up almost 100 feet below the house floor, and support a single truss, which we call a king truss. That king truss is unique because it is made up of the largest structural steel row sections that are available anywhere in the world. They had to be imported because there is only one steel company that rolls beams that large, or sections that large. The engineers and the architect basically designed the structure to support the ceiling by designing catwalks which followed the line of the ceiling.

"The structure was designed for zone 4 earthquake resistance, and the building is classified as an essential facility. This puts it in the category of fire stations and hospitals. We are in zone 3, so the owner chose to design for an additional safety factor by designing for zone 4 plus

"The other unique thing is the rostrum is wide open for about 150 foot of width. 152 feet apart are two gigantic king columns, 7 feet in diameter and heavily reinforced

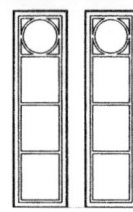

an additional 25% in order to classify it as an essential facility. What that really means in design terms is that if the building is struck by a zone 4 type earthquake, which is the worst you get in California or Japan or anyplace in the world, that the building might sustain damage, but it would not be taken out of service. In other words, it would still function and still be safe. That is the philosophy behind that design concept.

"The most difficult aspect of the project for me is that they cover up all my steel! It was a thing of beauty. I don't know if you've been up on the canopy, but you can get up right next to it and touch that king truss. I showed two of my old friends and colleagues the massive steel king and radial truss system and all they could say was 'Wow!'"

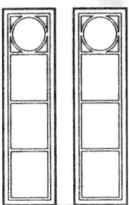

WORKERS, EQUIPMENT, & MATERIAL SUPPLIES

One of the most amazing aspects of the Conference Center project is the coordination and logistical management of thousands of workers, hundreds of pieces of equipment, and tons of material supplies. This is an especially amazing feat when you consider that all of this activity is taking place in the heart of downtown Salt Lake City.

The following four personal accounts by Paul Sandberg, George Ambrose, Lonnie Bullard and Sam Watterson give us a unique cross section of experiences and perspectives from four very different vantage points.

Paul Sandberg, chief scheduler for Legacy Constructors on the Conference Center project, gave this insight on juggling more that 7,500 different construction activities on this monumental building:

"My job has been the scheduling of all construction activities on this job site since June of 1997. Scheduling entails working with a lot of people. We sit down and talk about their areas and develop a sequence and durations for each activity that need to happen in their area, starting from the excavation through the concrete work and the structure, all the rough mechanical, electrical, plumbing, framing, drywall and right through to the finish detail work.

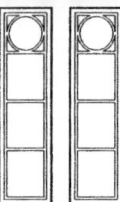

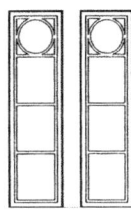

"Then we start bringing on the subcontractors. Currently, we have about 5,000 activities in the master schedule, and I have a lot of small schedules that go beyond that, another 2,500 to 3,000 activities. We try and status it once a week, and submit a copy to all the partners and the Church once a month for their review so they know where we're at. It's constantly changing.

"Jobs that have all of the design work completed up front, before we start construction, are a lot easier to plan. It's easier to procure materials and get your subcontractors lined up. In this case, design sometimes being behind construction, it makes things tough for us out here in the field. Literally we were getting faxes of plan details when we had concrete trucks standing out here to pour. We'd

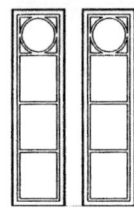

have to send the trucks back while we figured out where to relocate the framing. So it's been a challenge that way. And it's extremely challenging for the design team too. The architects have had at least 40 consulting engineers to help them design this project. It's extremely complex, and that trickles on through the construction end of it.

"When you pull a total city block out of the middle of a city, you are regulated with lay down areas and where you can put materials and how many workers and pieces of equipment you can physically get on the site. When we meet with subcontractors at the very beginning, we tell them that they can only bring materials enough for three days at a time, no more than that, because we're very limited to space. If everybody brought their materials out for the whole job, we would have no place to work. I'm extremely proud of what has happened here.

"I have an opportunity to work with the numbers that are involved with this building. We've poured 120,000 cubic yards of concrete. A normal home of about 2,500 square feet has approximately 100 cubic yards of concrete total in it so we're pouring the equivalent of 1,200 homes. There are 50,000 miles of electrical wire. All of that is housed in 780 miles of conduit, which is conduit from here to the California coast. Those types of numbers are very mind boggling to me."

George B. Ambrose is currently the Chief Operating Officer and Executive Vice President of Layton Construction Company, Inc. where he has worked for the

past 20 years. His comments of January 20, 2000:

"I was involved in all the partner meetings and my responsibility was to make sure there was a seamless relationship between Layton Construction Company, the work forces and the management of Legacy partnership. If we needed staffing, or additional field help, I was the one who coordinated the Layton resources to the Legacy joint venture.

"We realized that the Conference Center project was quite a bit larger than we'd anticipated, and it had a larger effect on our resources, because it took more people. With the many large freeway projects going on at the same time, taking lots of people out of this work force, it's amazing that we could get enough qualified help to come in and handle the responsibility that we were given. I think we have the very best subcontractors in the state of Utah on this project.

"Our construction schedule was compressed. We really needed to throw more men at it in a shorter period of time. They worked lots of overtime and second shifts. There came a real sense of urgency a year and a half ago to finish by April.

"The key has been the field superintendents who have worked with Harvey Wright to manage the manpower in each of the companies. The companies for the most part got along quite well. There is always competition between the craft workers in our business. There was a lot of pride there, and they fed off each other. It increased the

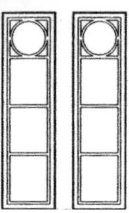

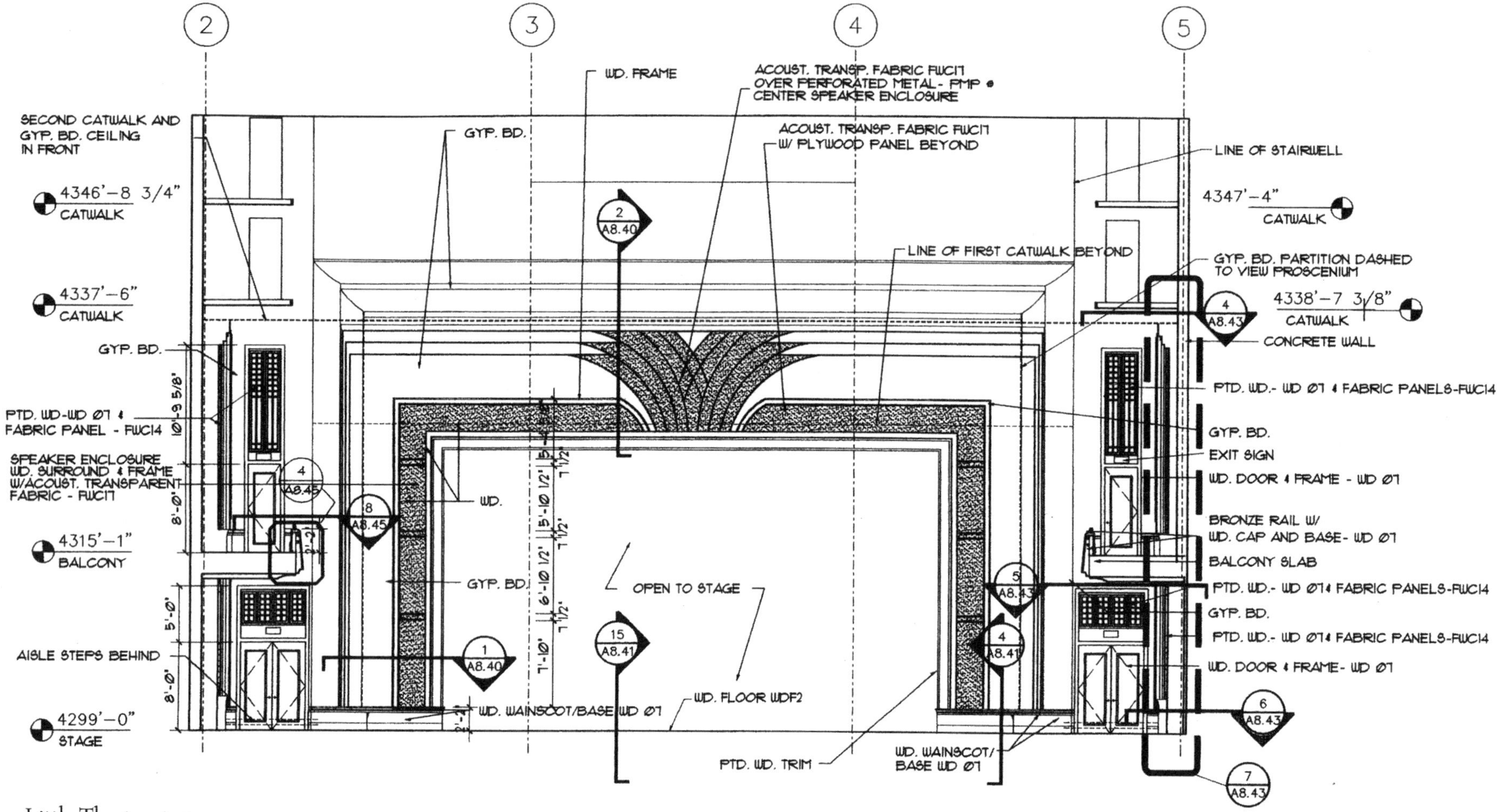

Little Theater stage.

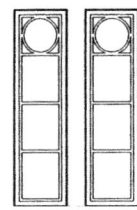

productivity and the quality of what they were doing, because they weren't about to be outdone by the other guys. When the challenge came, the guys would always say, "We can do this" even when it was a stretch. I compliment the way that all these people from different company cultures integrated and became committed emotionally to the common cause of this huge effort."

Lonnie M. Bullard is a partner in Legacy Constructors and is currently President and Chief Executive Officer of Jacobsen Construction Company, Inc. He commented on January 18, 2000:

"Shortly after our introduction to the project, it became clear to us that if President Hinckley wanted the project delivered by April 2000, it couldn't be done in the traditional method. We didn't have the time or luxury to wait for completed drawings before we started to build. That is not uncommon, but requires excellent communication and coordination between the owner, designers and contractor. All of the Legacy partners had completed projects on a "fast track" schedule. Fortunately, Jim Peterson and Harvey Wright had completed many projects that way.

"What was most unusual about this project was fast-tracking such a unique and one-of-a-kind building. If someone were to come into this office and say, 'I'd like you to build a retail shopping center.' We could generally ask a

series of questions and come pretty close to cost, what it would look like, how long it would take to design, and how long it would take to build. But for a project that has 21,000 seats in a theater setting, there was no comparable experience to make that leap! There was no one involved in the Conference Center who had extensive experience on similar projects. We all had experience with the components of the Center (i.e. heavy concrete frames, long span steel, theater seating, underground parking, etc.) but not in the magnitude and mass of this wonderful project.

"We knew early on it would be an aggressive schedule, and that Legacy would be operating under an at-risk contract. We knew that the Church wanted a professional business arrangment, and they would depend on us to get it done. At the beginning in 1996, some people said they thought an April 2000 completion date seemed like a long time to build a building. Upon closer examination of the magnitude of the project, however, they soon discovered that a lot of things had to come together very quickly in order for even that extended schedule to be met. By the time final selection was made and we were brought onboard, our schedule became approximately thirty-six months.

"All of us saw labor supply as a critical need for meeting the concrete schedule. The three Legacy partners felt by combining our labor forces we could succeed, but that would not be an easy process to go through. That level of cooperation does not happen very often because we are fierce competitors. It's one thing for the principals to get together and make the decision to join forces, but when you get several levels down it becomes more difficult. You could find a foreman or superintendent who wasn't part of the initial meetings and would not understand why the decision was made. To be required to work closely with companies they've competed against over the years was a difficult pill to swallow. We would wonder sometimes if it would work out.

Architectural rendering of Conference Center.

"We had a general idea what manpower would be required. We also had some strong opinions about how to

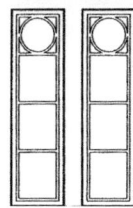

structure a joint venture of this kind. We knew that we couldn't divide the project into three pieces and say, "Jacobsen, you built that part; Okland, you build another part; and Layton, you build the third part". We knew that it had to be an integrated project team applying the best resources from each company. We knew it would take great leadership and supervision to put together a single cohesive management structure. We knew that to try to organize in another way was doomed to failure. It became a matter of trying to assess the personality and experience base of each management person available to see if a fit were there. That is easier to do when you know each of the people and their capabilities. We tried to do it where each partner knew his own forces, but where two-thirds of the people were not known to him.

"It was an interesting period. We put a management team together that has worked well. Jim and Harvey, for instance, have complementing strengths that we probably didn't fully anticipate when the match was made. They seem to work very well together and have built a tremendous rapport and respect for each other. That has been a critical part of the success of the project. They have done a wonderful job of providing experience and leadership to a very capable Legacy team. The principals have also stepped in and exhibited complementary strengths. Decisions have been made efficiently and without rancor. For the most part, we have tried to stay out of Jim and Harvey's way.

"I remember the first lunch we had for the workers

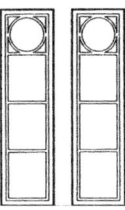

in the hole as we were beginning the concrete. I walked down and saw the Jacobsen and Okland and the Layton people. Each firm had about 120 people working at the time. Just to see the various backgrounds and nationalities in our combined workforce, when they were all there together, was a pretty remarkable sight. Later on, when we held a family open house, the sight was even more touching. To see these seasoned, calloused construction workers bringing their grandkids through, to see them with their children and spouses, pointing to certain places in the building and saying, That's where I work, trying to explain to them the overall project, and seeing the pride in their eyes, that was very rewarding. President Boyd K. Packer described Legacy to one of the partners by saying that it was as if Legacy yoked up the oxen. Each player had on a yoke and all were just pulling ahead. The three companies in tandem were getting the work done. That was refreshing and gratifying. It's a joint venture that has worked."

Steve Watterson operates the Western Automatic Sprinkler Company. Steve and four of his own sons worked together as members of the fire protection system installers on this project and represent a unique family involvement. He commented on Februrary 23, 2000:

"This is probably as far as fire sprinkler work goes, as tough as any job done in the valley. There are 15,000 sprinkler heads on this job and over 75 miles of sprinkler piping. Which is just an enormous amount of piping. There are 20 reaction systems. And there are 33 different zones

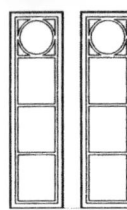

on this for a total of 53 separate zones on one building, which is far beyond anything we've done in my 30 years of experience. It's been a great project.

"My partner and our engineer is Bruce Hagen, and his son, Mark Hagen designed it. A very hard job to design. The design of the building, where it terraces down on the outside, creates a very nice garden and planting area. But on the inside of the building, it created a lot of problems for

Architectual mode of Conference Center in relation to Temple Square.

us to sprinkle. In a single room, you might have some sprinklers at 30 feet, and then you move over 30 feet and the next sprinkler is at 60 feet, because of the terrace on the outside of the building. It's a gorgeous building.

"The schedule has been a challenge. Having so short a time to do such a massive project. I think probably every contractor has faced that, getting good people, the right number of people on the job. We've been fortunate, we've got some good journeyman fitters who have done a great job on this project. In total we have had as many as thirty-one workers on this site at one time.

"I have five sons, four of them are working on the project with me. So for us, it's a legacy that we're going to leave. A lot of our LDS employees feel the same way. My

Model of rooftop landscaping.

whole ward knows that we're working on this. I am the Bishop of the ward and so with the hours we're working it's been hard to maintain my interview schedule. My counselors had to maintain a lot of the burden. But everybody is so interested in it. When we talk about it, everyone is just fascinated with the project. I just wish I could bring them all onto the site and let them see where their Bishop has been the last year. It's been a good project and it's meant something to us.

"There was a time a month and a half ago that I just didn't see how I could ever get the job done. And I took it to the Lord and said, I've got to have some help. One of our competitors called us and let us take three of his people, after that prayer. Because of those people we are in good shape. Just three extra journeymen that knew what they were doing made a big difference for us.

"Years ago we were working on the Logan Temple. And they were tearing down some old walls. Behind those old walls were the names of the workers that worked on the plaster walls. Since seeing that, I've thought they truly left a legacy for later generations. We are now doing the same thing. My grandchildren will see this wonderful building and probably my great grandchildren will see it 150 years from now. I want them to look at it and be proud of what I've done."

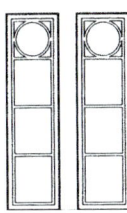

February 27, 1998.

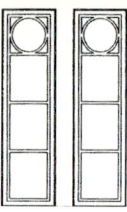

April 28, 1998.

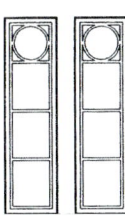

August 28, 1998.

September 28, 1998.

October 1998.

October 28, 1998.

October 1998.

October 1998.

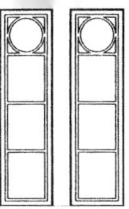

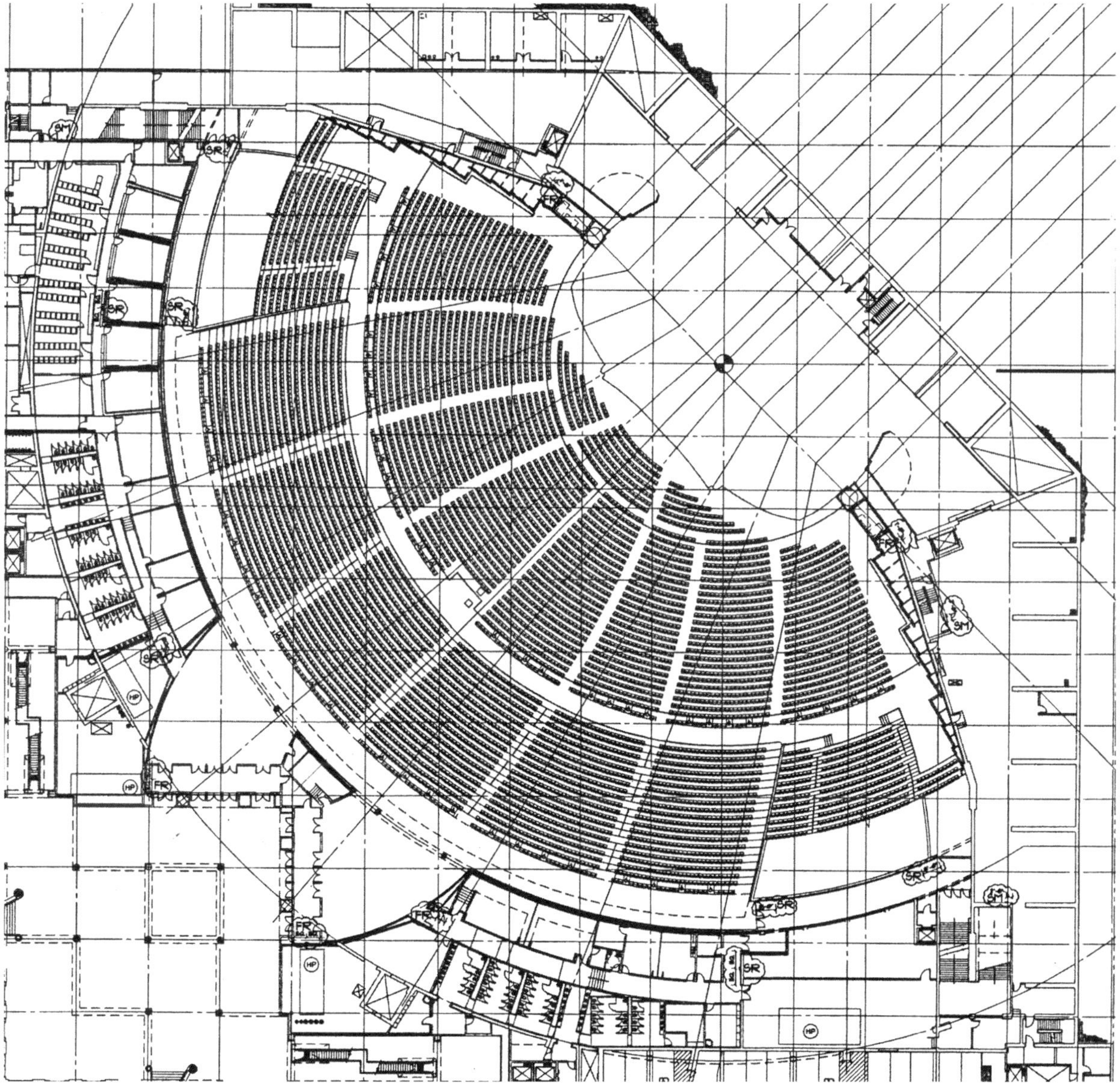

CHAPTER THREE
1999
AGAINST ALL ODDS

This year in the construction of the Conference Center was highly unusual from any viewpoint— an increased level of building activity; security concerns brought on by random acts of gun violence at the Triad Center and LDS Family History Library in Salt Lake City and if those weren't enough— a deadly and destructive F2-strength tornado which passed through the construction site.

The following newspaper article by Ray Boren appeared in the <u>Deseret News</u> on January 30, 1999: "Shoulders To The Wheel At LDS Assembly Hall. We broke ground on July 24, 1997, and we're scheduled to complete it on April 1, 2000 in time for the annual general conference of The Church of Jesus Christ of Latter-day Saints, said Kerry B. Nielsen, project architect.

"Even as some design work continues, crews are laboring with that target date in mind. That's just under three years. The Tabernacle went up in three years and three months; the [Salt Lake] temple took 40 years.

FACTS & STATS

- Heating/cooling systems source from off-site plant.
- The HVAC system had nearly 3,000 tons of air conditioning or enough for 600 homes.
- Every minute 1,035,000 cubic feet of air is moved through 14 miles of HVAC duct work.
- Electronically enhanced audio system (ERES).
- Fully equipped theatrical systems (lighting, sound, and rigging).
- 50,000 miles of wire, 780 miles of conduit, and 4,000 amp services.
- Emergency diesel generator (output 2,000 kilowatts).
- Television and radio broadcast studio capabilities with digital high definition.

Interior of Conference Center auditorium.

Today, workmen, who look no larger than dolls from a distance, can be seen on the top of the low-profile assembly building roof. They are preparing forms, pouring and smoothing concrete, sometimes first shifting chunks of winter ice and piles of snow out of the way.

"Inside, engulfed by the dark and cavernous auditorium, a laden semitrailer-truck is parked, resembling a distant Tonka toy amid a small forest of construction cranes. Near the biggest of these, called a *sky horse*, steelworkers are assembling a massive truss. This, the last of 10 such roof-supporting spans, is expected to go up in the coming week. The other nine, ranging up to 280 feet

long and weighing 550 tons, are in place high above and radiate like sunbeams from the muscular 621-ton "king truss" over the rostrum area.

"Elsewhere on the 10-acre block (a few more of you count the incremental creep of equipment and office trailers onto bordering streets), welders can be seen securing beams and bars, sparks flying, as electricians and technicians install conduits and wiring and spray crews fireproof the structural steel. Masons have already begun hanging the first Little Cottonwood Canyon-granite panels on exterior walls. Precast concrete pieces, like steps, are being put on risers in the great hall, so the future sea of seats— 21,000 in all— can be installed. Many of the 600 construction workers negotiate mid-winter mudholes and shallow swamps. Come spring there will be about 800 workers each day on the busy site. . . .

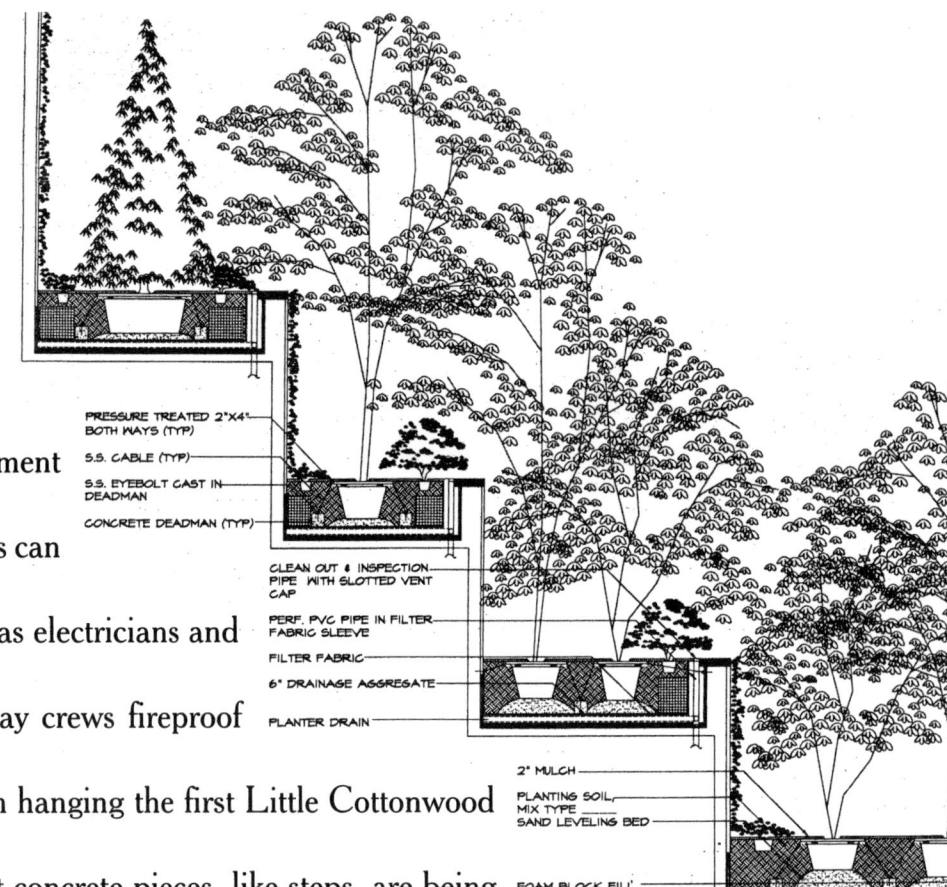

North Terraced Planters--section.

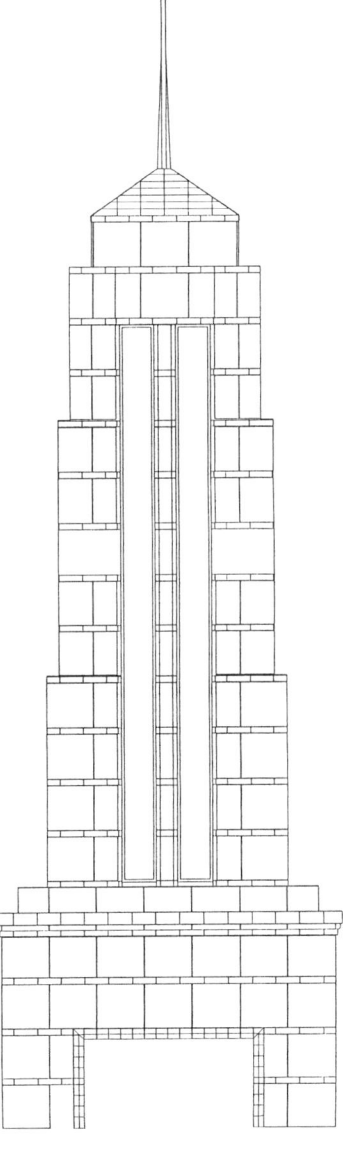

"Right now the interior space, without seating or pulpit, seems boundless. 'A Boeing 747 could fit in the hall, nose to tail and wing to wing,' said construction manager Gary Holland. 'You could probably fit two of them in there if they were positioned just right.'

"The facility's eye-catching exterior features will include its single spire and the rooftop gardens, said Kerry Nielsen. Four park-like acres with flower- and tree-filled planters, plazas, walking paths and fountains. The space on top of this building is unprecedented, he continued. The crown jewel is still the Salt Lake Temple, but this building's landscaping will focus attention toward the south and will provide incredible vistas of Temple Square and the downtown skyline that have never been seen before."

Tornados aren't supposed to touch down in Utah. But there was Bill Alder, the chief meteorologist for the National Weather Service in Utah, watching his radar screen with growing concern just after lunch on Wednesday, August 11th. "It looked like severe weather and that can generate funnel clouds which can turn into a tornado," he said. "But that doesn't happen here in Salt Lake City, Utah."

THE TORNADO OF '99

Just before 1 p.m., a twister ripped through the heart of the city destroying more than 300 homes and businesses and killing one man, Allen Crandy, an exhibitor at the Outdoor Retailers Summer Market. The tornado winds reached speeds of 150 miles per hour and its terrible swath of destruction, some three miles long and a half-mile wide, proved devastating to the Delta Center, Wyndham Hotel, Dee's Restaurant, the Conference Center construction site and then up to the State Capitol grounds and Memory Grove where dozens of magnificent trees were blown to the ground.

J. Randy Okland, one of the principals of the Legacy Constructors, gave this first-hand account of surviving the tornado which struck the Conference Center site as he and others were there:

"The day the tornado occurred the Legacy partners were having one of our regular Wednesday meetings. That particular day was just like most any other day, but as we were sitting there it seemed to get a little bit windy and then you could see that it was getting darker outside. We were in the trailer which was to the west of the project at West Temple. We have four temporary trailers and they have a

(Courtesy of Chris Evans)

common roof built in between them to make a walkway. It kept getting darker and we just sat there talking, and then the lights went out in the trailer a couple of times. Everybody just thought somebody had driven over the cord or something.

"It was getting darker and the winds came like mad. We all jumped up from the table and started looking outside. We could see everything blowing by the windows and I don't think any of us really knew what to do. We looked out at the cranes and saw those tower cranes up there and knew how high they were in the air. One thing we knew is that we shouldn't be close to the glass. So we got back away from the windows. There were things being blown towards some people and we invited a few of them into the

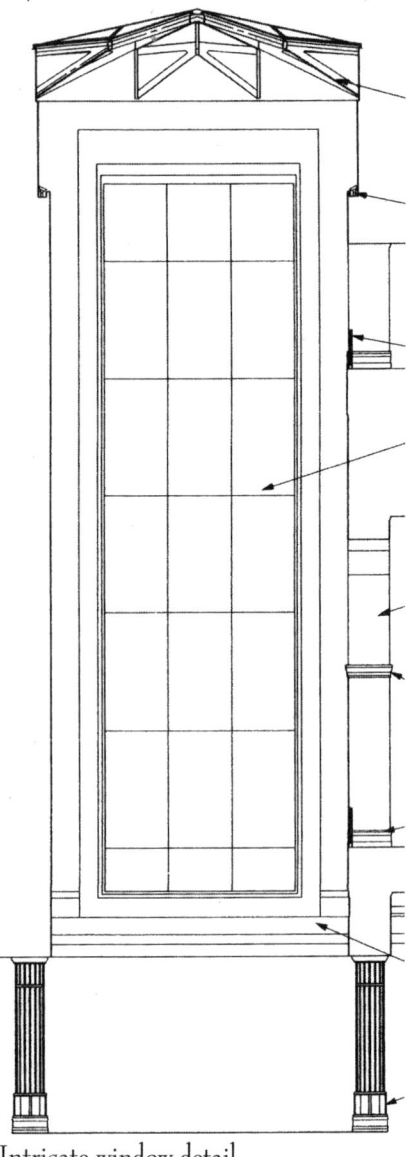

Intricate window detail.

trailer. A minute later it all passed. It blew out a window in the end of a trailer. Had it hit the trailer directly, I don't know what would have happened, because we were not prepared or anchored for anything like that.

"Then I looked back out the window and there was no boom on the yellow crane. The fortunate thing was that the crane operator in the other crane and one of the crane operators on the Little America project which was being done a few blocks away, have radio communication with each other. They saw the storm coming and they warned our workers by radio. We had nearly 1,000 people on the site at the time the tornado struck. The scaffolding was all bent, the crane boom blew down and landed on the building and yet there were only four injuries to our workers.

"The Lord was watching over us on that day. The tornado came right over the top of some of the church buildings. It missed the Temple grounds and went diagonally, right across this building. Just thirty seconds before this happened there were probably forty people

working on the exterior stone work dangling on the scaffolding. Because of the radios and the quick thinking of the men on the job site notifying each other, everybody was able to get inside the building. A man who was a traffic guard up on the corner of Main Street and Second North was hit by some debris along with some other people in that area. Unfortunately they weren't within the radio communication with others on the site.

"The trailer next to our trailer was actually lifted up and moved over a couple of feet. We could feel ours lift and the windows were blown out. We went outside after and saw trees blown down, and tool boxes that weighed hundreds of pounds, thousands of pounds some of them, just blown over into different parts of the project. The building itself received very little damage considering the force and power of that tornado. The crane was damaged but even where the crane fell on the building, it didn't do that much damage to the Conference Center itself. It could have set that project back months or more, but the work crews had it cleaned up in just a few days and we were back in full swing.

"The operator of the crane that received the most damage had to run an errand that day and wasn't in the crane when the storm hit. The crane operator in the second crane got down underneath it in the ring gear and braced himself, while the crane boom was lifted up by the force of the tornado. Luckily that crane didn't suffer any damage. It was a miracle there weren't a lot of serious injuries to the

Conference Center workers on that fateful day."

Another eyewitness description of the tornado was given by Alan S. Layton:

"Those of us that have lived here in Salt Lake City know about summer thunder storms. As we were meeting in the trailer west of the project, we could tell that we were going to have one of those wild summer afternoon thunder storms that develop and blow through. I felt the winds blow, saw the driving rain and saw boxes and things that were lightweight moved around the trailer complex, I still didn't see it as any more than just a micro burst of a thunderstorm. We looked out the window and we could feel things blowing around. I looked up and saw that the yellow crane didn't appear to have it's boom on it. I said, The yellow crane has lost its boom. Then we went outside and we could see that the damage was far more severe than maybe anticipated. I happened to have a little raincoat in my truck and I went down into the parking structure and put that on with a hard hat. I began to walk inside and people were talking about a tornado. I went with our safety director to the roof to make sure the building was cleared and see if there was anybody hurt, what happened to the crane boom, and to check on the damage to the building. We were fortunate that the boom had landed on some planters. If you had to take the boom off and lay it on the roof, you couldn't have picked a more favorable spot.

"The damage to the building was really very nominal. Visibly, no one was hurt, but from the top of the roof we could see all of the emergency vehicles down by the Salt Palace and the motel. Across the street we could see the tents of an outdoor retailers' exposition were shredded and that there were lots and lots of trees down. We saw that a lot of our Styrofoam was up on the lawn of the McCune Mansion. It stopped raining after a half hour

Tornado damage on Conference Center.

or so and we just got to work cleaning up and moving on. It wasn't until later that I realized that it literally was a tornado.

"We were worried about the crane that lost its boom. They are designed with the boom that you work under, and what's called a counter bridge that is on the opposite side of the tower. They balance each other. When they're erected they go up sequentially in pieces so that the tower is in balance all the time. Taking the boom off the tower greatly stressed it in one direction and we were concerned that it might fall over. We learned later from the crane company that in all their years they've never had something like this happen before, although they've had literally hundreds of cranes in the air. Even during Hurricane Andrew in Florida, they've never had this happen."

The following is Legacy Constructors partner, Ted M. Jacobsen's account:

"We were all in an office trailer with the windows facing to the east. The tornado came from the west so we had no forewarning. Fortunately a lot of the workers could see it coming because the building was open on the west side. That was a lucky thing because they were able to get out of harms way for the most part. In our case, we were having a meeting discussing the project. All of a sudden the sky darkened and it started to rain very hard. When I looked outside it was clear that there were high winds, and all sorts of construction materials were floating 50 or 100

feet in the air and flying around. It was clearly a very dangerous situation! The trailer started to shake and it felt like it was going to move. We could hear lots of cracking, breaking, twisting and turning and the voices of people who were scurrying to get to shelter.

"I didn't see the funnel cloud of the tornado because I was right in the middle of it. So we just hung on and waited until it was over, because there was nothing we could do. I thought of the scene from the *Wizard of Oz* and expected Dorothy's crotchety school teacher from Kansas to pedal by the window in the air at any moment. As quickly as it started, it was over. It only lasted a minute. We went outside and the trailer complex had been badly damaged. Some of the temporary toilets were tipped over. Then I looked up into the area where the yellow tower crane should have been and it wasn't there anymore and my heart sunk.

"Our workers and their supervisors did a very good job of quickly getting the site under control and then identifying the few people that were injured on site and getting them to care. There was a lady across the street who had been hurt by a tree branch that had broken off, and other injuries occurred nearby. Our workers helped cordon off areas that were dangerous. There was a metal enclosure that had blown off the top of the Church Museum of Art and History that was dangling up in a tree, and people were walking under it not seeing it, and so we got

that closed off and cleared the branches off the streets so emergency vehicles could get around. It was an interesting experience. That night as I watched on television the films of our tower crane going down, it was just an amazing feeling to see the power of the wind and realize how very fortunate and blessed we were that more people weren't hurt and that more damage wasn't done. Our workers handled themselves very well that day."

LDS Church architect, Kerry Nielsen, gave the following insight to the events during and after the impact of Salt Lake City's first recorded tornado and the damage it caused to the Conference Center project:

"Where was I on August 11, 1999? I was on the roof of the building twenty minutes before it hit. Two hours before the tornado hit, I had the LDS Relief Society, Primary, and Young Women's general boards and two members of the Presiding Bishopric in the Conference Center. It hit about 1:00 or so. I was on the roof with one of the superintendents dealing with an issue and made the comment, 'Gosh, it looks yuckie out there. We're going to get one of those summer thunderstorms.' We were just going inside the building on the balcony level where all the glass is, and all of a sudden it went dark, there was a lot of noise and things started hitting the window. I knew it was the storm we'd seen coming. There was a bunch of chatter on the radio to take cover. We couldn't understand what was

going on. I yelled, 'Get inside the hall!' We went in on the balcony level and went inside the shear wall, that big radial wall. And just about then it really hit. The lights went down and started to flicker, and the noise level went up and you could hear things smacking into the glass outside the lobby.

"The building tried to pressurize, but it couldn't. Luckily we were still open enough. It didn't create the

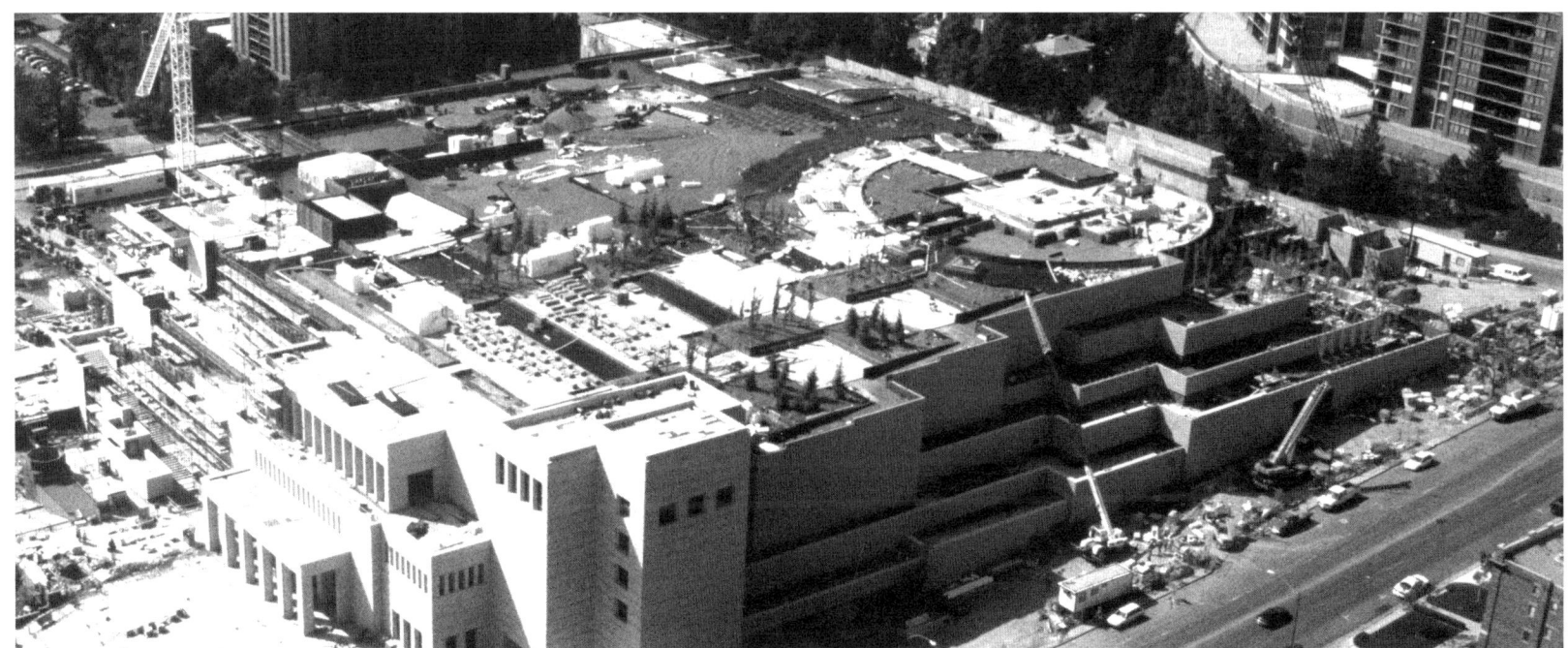

Aerial shot of Conference Center--September 1, 1999.

vacuum outside where the building explodes. In a tornado buildings don't implode, they explode, because the pressure outside goes to almost zero. We had some materials blown up one of the stairwells and it pushed two guys through the door. I saw that just before it went completely black. In about 30 seconds, it went from daylight and noise to a room with no power. It was chaos. We were choking on the dust, we could hardly breathe. And it was a complete black out. I could hear people yelling and calling and I said, 'Just stay put, guys. You're on solid ground. Don't move'. It took about another 30 or 45 seconds and the noise went away, but we heard this big building shake over our heads. It was the crane hitting the deck.

"We heard some loud yelling again. I had the flash of the worst possible thing I could imagine happening. We had a lot of people on site that day and I knew that whatever had just happened wasn't good. We had to wait another 30 seconds and all of a sudden I started to see some pin hole lights start to open up. We had openings I could see out into the lobby. It was supposed to be daylight but it was black. There was such a combination of clouds, storm and dust, it took another minute or so for the dust to settle, and we could see enough to walk out. I ran out in the lobby again to see what was going on. I could see some damage and some people scrambling. I tried to get out on my cell phone, but the lines were tied up. I went out in the

building and could see a piece of crane hanging there.

"Legacy was really organized. They had a safety team that came out in procedure and cleared the site. We had that crane hanging on the building in an incredibly precarious position. It was balanced just enough that it didn't go over. If it would have gone down completely, it would have caused havoc no matter which way it fell. In the 1980s in Dallas, Texas I was on a project site and saw a crane go over and many men died that day, so I knew we had a serious problem.

"Harvey Wright, Chris Bardin and a man by the name of Dave Miller, who is the lead foreman for Schuff Steel put their heads together and made a plan. That afternoon they mobilized Wagstaff Crane and some other guys and that's part of this miracle. They pulled this group together and they worked through the night and into the next day to do all the rigging. I went home late at night, ate dinner and tried to do some work. I had taken radios with me to try to keep in touch with Harvey Wright. I certainly wasn't in command, but I felt like I had a responsibility here.

"When I talked to the job, Harvey said, 'We're going to get this crane down tonight'. So I came back to the site to check on them and then went home again. I ended up coming back and spending the night because I couldn't even think straight. I couldn't settle down, so I paced North Temple all night long. It started to be cold up there, the wind was blowing and things got a little dicey. I gave one of the riggers working with Dave my coat so they could work without shivering. I'll tell you, Harvey and Chris and Dave were pretty high on my list that day. I would give them credit for making the tornado incident a non-disaster for the Conference Center and its workers. Those three guys put themselves on the line that night. That's the truth.

"That's a day I won't forget for a long time, if ever. The building has been designed for seismic zone 4 plus an

Crane damaged in tornado.

importance factor. I would have gone on record in front of anyone saying this building would be tested by an earthquake before it ever got tested by a tornado, but I was wrong. It was an amazing thing. We had 1,000 people and only four injuries, two were serious, two others were fairly minor, and they all ended up okay. Getting the stone out of the mountain was the first miracle, this was the second."

Chris Bardin is the chief safety officer on the Conference Center project and therefore has a particularly interesting perspective on the tornado experience:

Translator booths design.

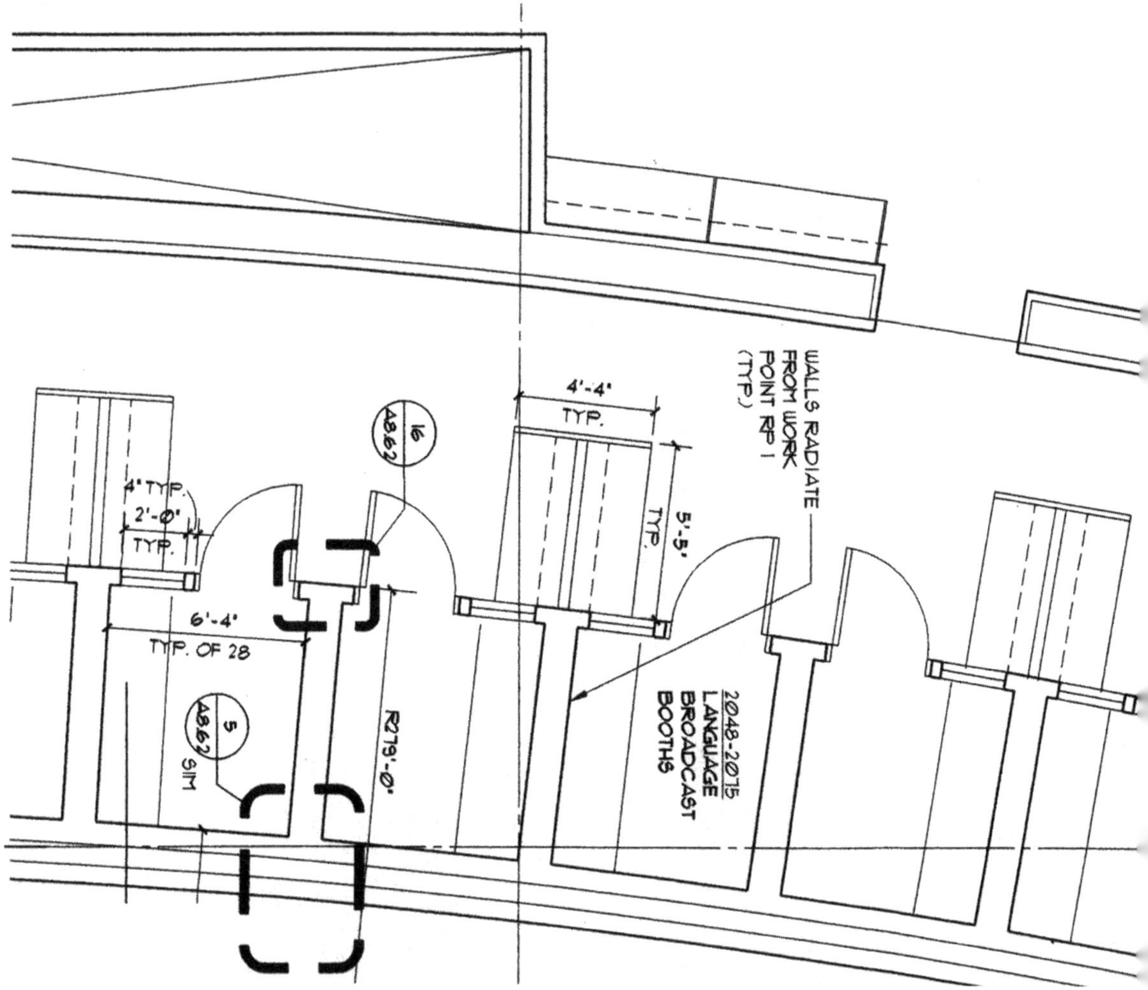

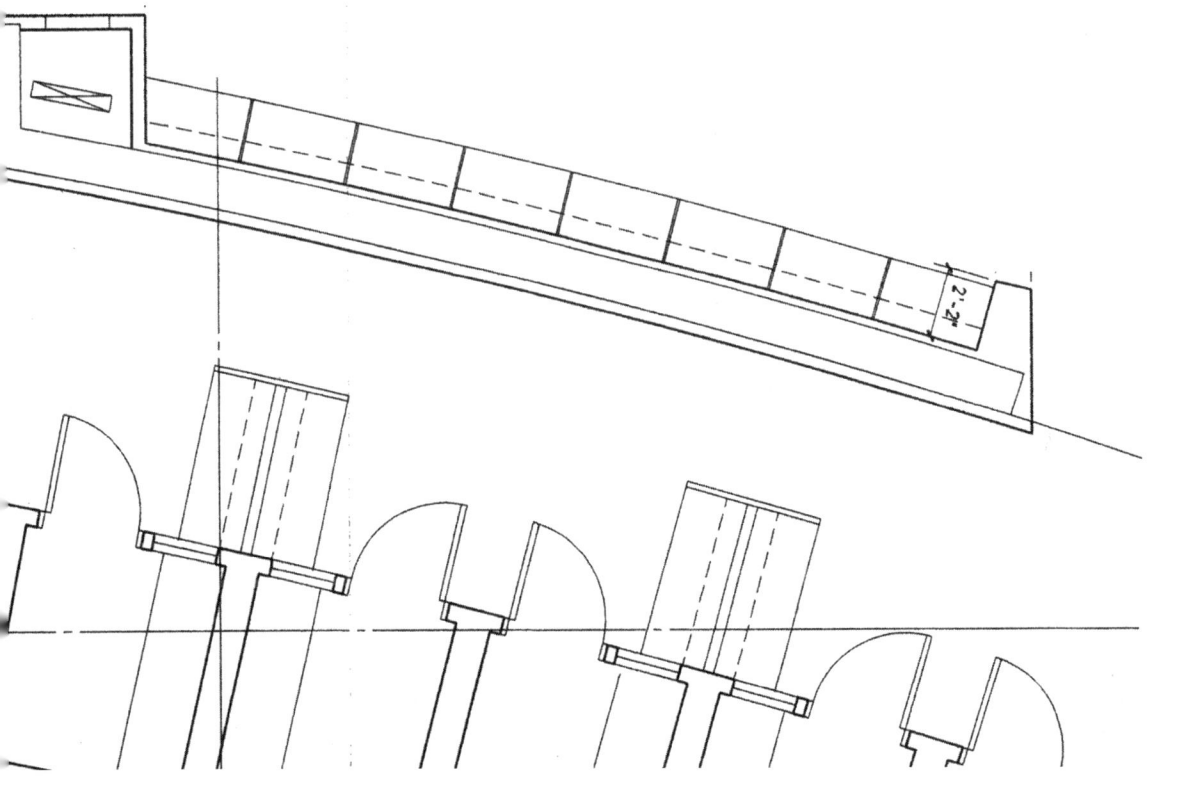

"On most large projects, like the Conference Center there is an emergency program. I've never considered a tornado, although we prepare for a fire or a major explosion. We designed a method of identifying who came into work that day, for an emergency head count. Prior to the tornado, we had established two areas, one on the east side of the project and a parking lot on the west side that were the muster areas if we ever had a disaster. That's where all the employees were to go. The foremen were to take a head count and they were to get back to their Legacy coordinators on exactly how many men were accounted for and how many were missing. The plan worked very well. That's exactly what we did.

"The tornado hit as we were coming back onto the property from lunch. We'd been on site just a few minutes. We were getting back into

our day over on the Second North side when my partner Bruce McFarland, the field safety coordinator said, "That storm is twisting". We all looked and I thought, "That thing is spinning". It came across their radio to get in the building because the crane operator in the white tower crane could tell that it was a tornado. That gave us the few seconds we had. We got on our company radios and just started telling everybody to get in the building, get down, and get out of the way, and within thirty seconds that thing hit the building.

"We were close to our trailer so we got in and away from the windows. The noise was very loud. We knew that it wasn't just a high wind storm; the debris was bouncing off the trailer and hitting the windows and then just as quickly it was gone. Immediately after that we went outside and the minute we opened the doors, someone said that the yellow tower crane was down. Talk about high adrenaline kicking in! To have a crane down is usually death. You can't imagine what was going through my mind.

"We got on the radios and got all the safety people of all the companies that were on our frequency. We gathered them up and started at the yellow tower crane assessing damages. We immediately cleared the building so that we could get a head count, and told everybody to get in to the safe areas, which we call the muster areas, to start that process. We made sure there wasn't anyone under the tower

crane, and soon we heard that the operator had been at lunch. We grabbed different groups of employees and set them out at different intersections to stop traffic. People were running all over, but we stopped all the pedestrians. We wanted to make sure that any downed power lines were sealed.

"After we got the building cleared, we conducted a Porta-John check. We had a number of those units on this job that were tipped upside down, and it would be a heck of a place to be trapped.

"We had to keep a lane open on North Temple for ambulances because that is the main thoroughfare to the hospitals. We didn't have any FM/AM type radios so we had no idea what had happened in other places, but we saw some Davis County ambulances and we knew something major was going on. I had a couple of contractors with heavy equipment and we got the roads cleared in a hurry so that we could allow the Emergency Medical Systems (EMS) to work on Second North and on West Temple. There was debris scattered all the way to the State Capitol.

"We had a flagger who was at the intersection of Main Street and Second North. He was attempting to get into a tool trailer when a large foam block blew off the top of the roof, struck him and knocked him down. He ended up with a concussion. We got him to the hospital as well as

all the other folks that were injured there.

"We had about 950 workers on the job site that day and we had everybody out of the building and accounted for. At that point, we sent everybody home. We only allowed a few back in the building by paths that we knew were safe, for medications or car keys. All the gang boxes and all the tools, we left like it was. Then the following morning we allowed the supervisors in after we had spent the afternoon and most of the night safetying off everything. It was very organized, everything was locked up and it worked quite well.

"We actually had a total of five people seen by a doctor. There is no doubt in my mind, God's hand was over this project. No doubt in my mind. Anybody asks me, that's what I'll tell them too."

James Peterson, Legacy's construction executive, gives this account: "We witnessed a miracle when we had a tornado come through Salt Lake City. The tornado was dead centered on this building and although it caused us a couple of days setback, the damage was minimal. We had about $1 million damage, but most of that cost was in the tower crane that fell. We

> "There is no doubt in my mind, God's hand was over this project. No doubt in my mind."

had one of our tower crane's "lifting arm" blown off. It hit the top of the roof. The workers that were on the roof got about a thirty-second warning and ran into the roof portico up on the southeast corner of the building. As the crane fell down it missed that portico by about six feet. It went across a couple of the planters and broke a hole in one spot and chiseled some grooves into the planters, but did only minor damage.

"The flying debris was a problem. We had a lot of insulation on the roof, big blocks of Styrofoam, and most of that ended up in the neighborhood around the State Capitol. We began a clean up effort.

"The tornado came right over the top of the Dee's restaurant and right straight across us. Then it jumped up again, before it dropped down into the Capitol Hill/Memory Grove area. We feel very fortunate that there were no serious injuries on this job site."

George Ambrose, who had experienced other tornados in Texas, described the event as follows:

"I was sitting in the partners' meeting in the trailer, and remember someone yelling to us that a tornado was going to hit. Other than Jim Peterson and myself, I don't think any of the other partners had ever experienced a tornado before. I was raised in Texas and the Midwest and had been around them. Having lived in Utah for over twenty years, I didn't think the alarm was true. When we

stood up our trailer started to move, and we saw the debris flying as the trailer next to us got its windows blown out, I could see that it was pretty serious. I am very thankful that I was in the second trailer.

"We're building a heat plant for the Conference Center that will supply all the steam and chilled water, and the tornado hit that project too. It received much more damage. As I walked around the project after the tornado passed, I felt like Salt Lake City had been bombed. People were dazed. It was really an eerie feeling. Everything was unconnected. People were walking around bloody and dazed and I really felt like I had been in some kind of an explosion. Thank goodness that those guys got off the scaffolding. They were four stories high! We were very lucky that day.

"The safety people got everyone organized and did a marvelous job. It was something that you never plan for, on a project in Utah. I was impressed with the way they cordoned off the crane and got everyone out of the building. Each of the companies went to a certain area and it was done well.

"The structure of the Conference Center itself was sound. Maybe that was a little test that the Lord gave the building. It's supposed to be a 150 year building. Well, it certainly passed that test."

While the force of Mother Nature hurled its mighty

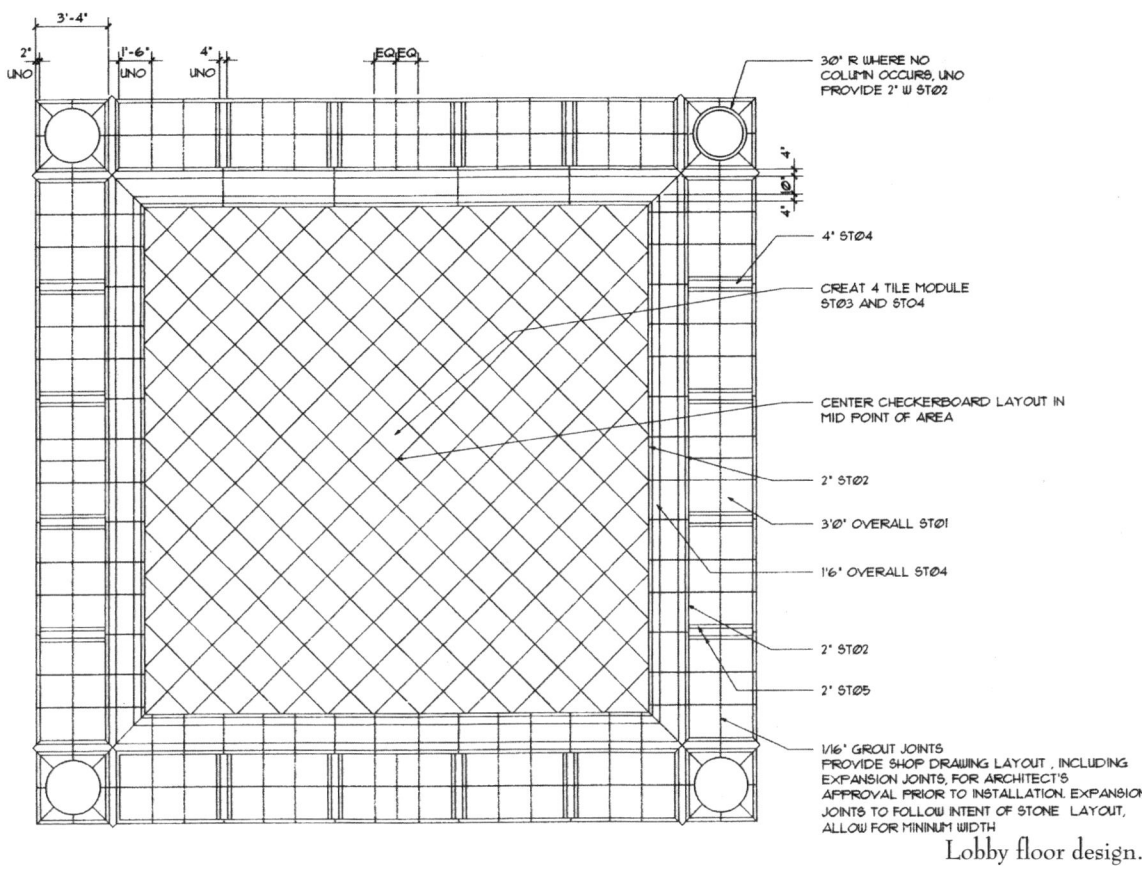
Lobby floor design.

winds, the construction crews numbering nearly 1,000 continued to meet the "normal" challenges. Working long hours during six-day-work-weeks, these men and women of the Legacy Constructors and their subcontractors struggled to meet demanding deadlines. Here are some of their accounts and "construction stiff" perspectives:

Jay Starley is a supervisor for the Parry Olsen Drywall Company. His description of creating the finished sheet rock interior space directly beneath the nine skylights in the Conference Center while

suspended 180 feet above the lobby floor gave a very unique perspective on the designer / builder relationship.

"Our company's biggest challenge was definitely the framing and sheet rocking of the shafts beneath each of the nine skylights. We suspended our 30 by 30 working platforms more than 180 feet above the floor. We used 40 foot studs, 6 inch, 18 gauge steel, and had a wench hooked up on the floor with a guy down there doing the cutting. He would raise the studs and the sheet rock up to the working platforms with a hoist. It would take four minutes to raise up a stud or two pieces of sheet rock, whatever you were lifting up there. And two minutes from the platform to the top of the skylight.

"The designers hadn't thought of the difficulty of raising the materials up to the height of our working platforms. Not once did the architects say, 'How do you get the sheet rock up there? How do you get the studs up there?'

"The first skylight took us just about a month to do.

Working on interior lobby walls.

142

And we got them down to two weeks, framed, rocked and taped. They were definitely a challenge and scary. I lost a lot of sleep over those. I built those every night. It was real controversial whether they could be done or not. The church architects didn't want the skylights at first. But the architects thought they would be the main feature. So now they're glad they were left in. I've been here over a year with sixty-five of our workers."

Roger Gukeisen is the superintendent for DAW Drywall Company with more than thirty years experience in the construction industry. He and his crew were responsible for the hanging, taping and finishing of 2,000,000 square feet of sheet rock for the interior walls and ceilings of the Conference Center. He said:

"I am the superintendent for Daw. I have had up to eighty-five men framing the walls, and hanging and finishing the sheet rock on the outside of the radial wall on this Conference Center project.

"I guess the most interesting highlight of this project was when the tornado went through. I was in my office, thank goodness. But it scared quite a few of the guys. We heard it come on the radio and could hardly believe it. I've lived in Salt Lake 50 years, all my life, and never seen a tornado of this magnitude here. I've got one guy that is my sheet rock foreman and this guy is a joker. He came over the radio saying there was a tornado coming through and we all just laughed at him until it did! So that was the most

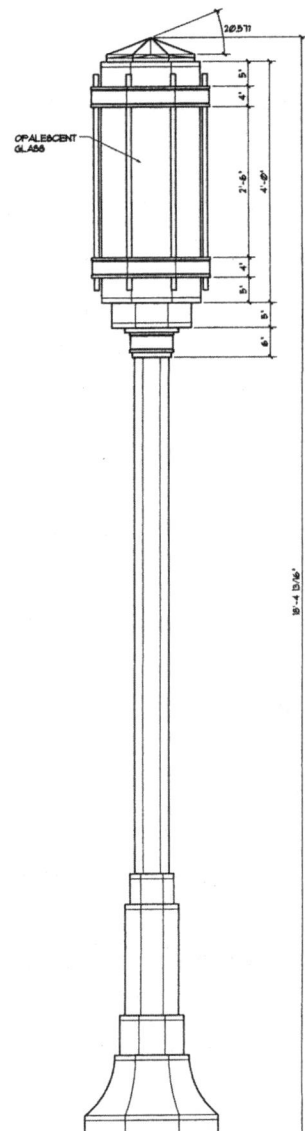

memorable time of the job.

"Just hanging 12 foot flat ceilings has been a challenge to a lot of our people. It's been a had job. It's been stressful. It's put a lot of us to being ornery at times. Over a period of years I learned to try and leave the job on the job for my family's sake. In fact today is my anniversary and I've been married 32 years.

"I've been in the building business for thirty-one years. So I have seen a lot of jobs and I have seen a lot of stuff that people wanted done that virtually was impossible. And I guess I always stand by the statement that it just takes a little longer to do the impossible. I honestly didn't think they'd finish this job by April of 2000. There has been a lot of work done on this building from when I arrived a year and a half ago. I now think that we'll make it after all."

One of the largest contractors on the Conference Center job is GSL Electric Company, whose project manager, Guy Moore, provided this *in the trenches* insight:

"We have about 170 electricians on site right now. That's our peak. We're starting to go the other way a little

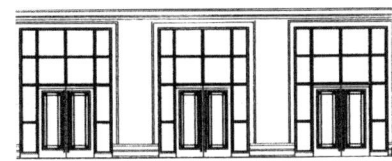

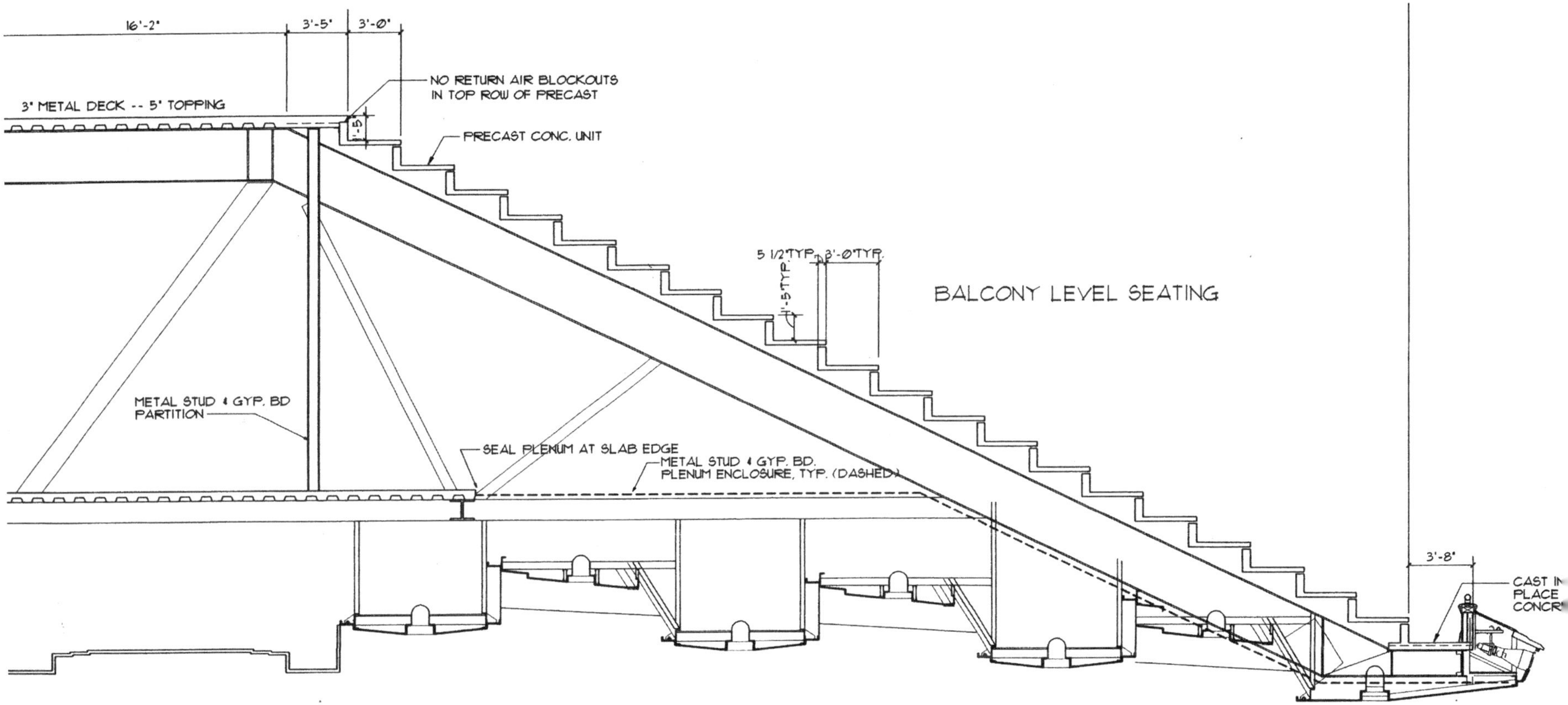

16'-2"
3'-5"
3'-0"
NO RETURN AIR BLOCKOUTS IN TOP ROW OF PRECAST
3" METAL DECK -- 5" TOPPING
1'-5"
PRECAST CONC. UNIT
5 1/2"TYP. 3'-0"TYP.
1'-5"TYP.
BALCONY LEVEL SEATING
METAL STUD & GYP. BD PARTITION
SEAL PLENUM AT SLAB EDGE
METAL STUD & GYP. BD. PLENUM ENCLOSURE, TYP. (DASHED)
3'-8"
CAST IN
PLACE

bit, but we've been over 100 for quite a while. We would like to have peaked earlier than we did, but problems with the concrete and steel just didn't allow that. Now we're trying to make up time.

"It's a tremendously interesting job. There is a lot of electrical work in it. We've got over 45,000 feet of four inch pipe running across the ceiling in the assembly hall. And that pipe all has large conductor wires in it. There is just a lot of weight up there. It's been very interesting from a standpoint of the magnitude of it. It's state of the art that they're going with on the audio and the broadcast. From that standpoint it's been very interesting.

"We had a challenge two or three months ago of finding enough qualified people to work on this project. There is a lot of construction work going on in our area and so that made it a challenge.

"We've managed to put together excellent leadership on this job. We've divided this project into about a dozen smaller pieces, with a foreman over each of the areas. So it's just like managing twelve little jobs, instead of one big one.

"I'm expecting the main difficulty to be the amount of energy it will take to pull this job off by April 1. It's a short time frame to get our work done.

"I think the workers have been glad to be a part of this building. I think they're proud of their work. From a

leadership standpoint, it's been a pleasure to work with the various men and women from the different companies. It's been a good experience. You always have your battles over territories and schedules, but they go away. I hope most of the workers feel some of the spirituality of this project."

Marty Gibbs is a supervisor for the B & T Masonry Company, which was the contractor for installing the processed granite veneer and concrete block materials on the Conference Center.

"We installed all the concrete masonry units (CMU) on the interior of the building. Then we did all the split faced ashlar, which is the rough-finished granite stone on the exterior on the east elevation and the north elevation, along with all the caps. The ashlar granite

Escalator design.

came in pallets, weighing roughly 4,500 to 5,000 pounds in random lengths. Anywhere from twelve inches up to four foot. They were four inches thick. We just put those up on the scaffold, and our forty-two brick layers hammered and chiseled those pieces to fit.

"The best thing is just being able to say that you've been part of it, actually working with the material that came out of the mountain. The same material that built the original

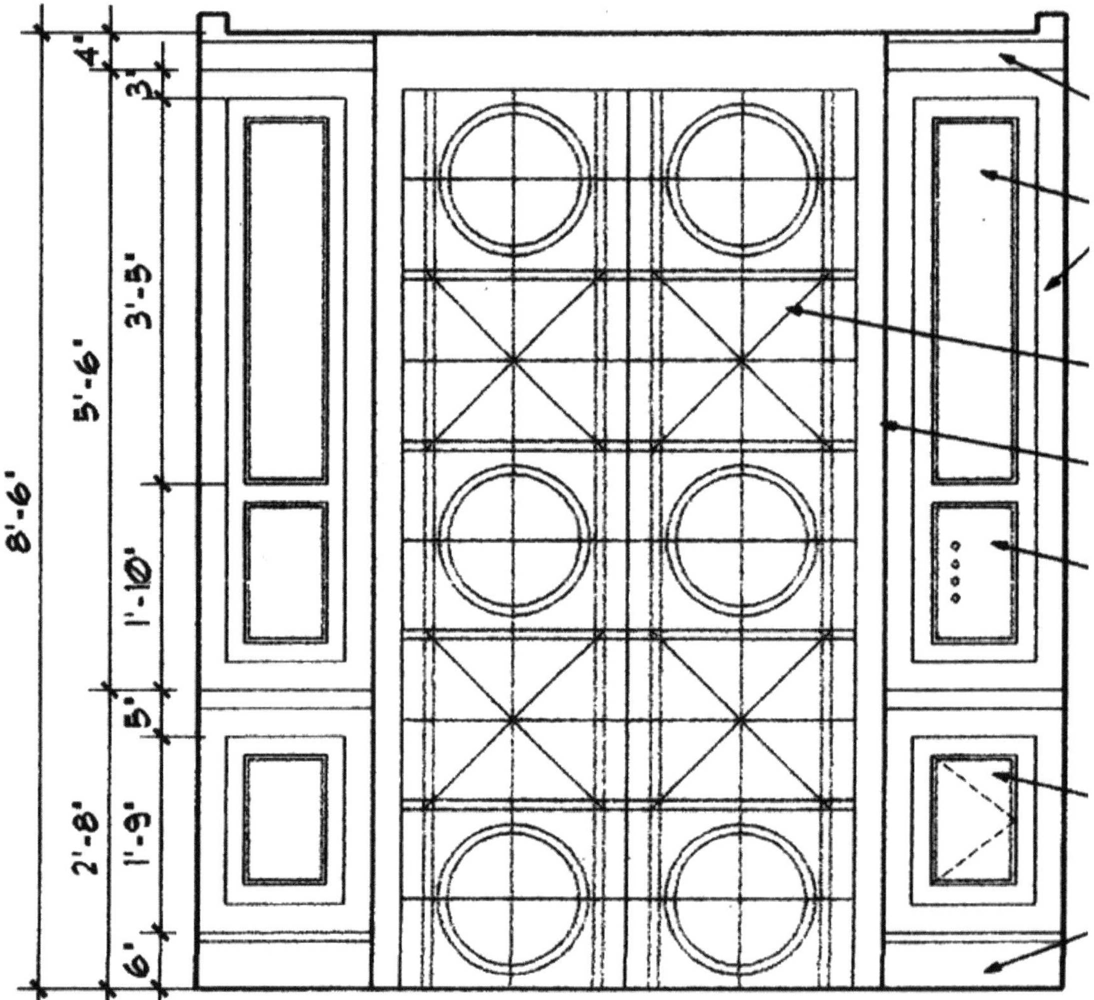

Elevator door design.

148

temple is really something. It's a feather in my cap. We've had a struggle with the schedule. Anybody that has worked on this job will tell you that it's been tough right from the very start to try to make this April 1st deadline.

"There was so much up front work that had to be done before we could come in and put the finishing touches on. I look at the stone as basically five inches of paint. The building has to be there and all we're doing is putting five inches of paint on it. It's been a struggle at times for the other contractors to stay ahead of us. They've done a real good job on this enormous project.

"The weather we've had these last couple of seasons is a miracle. I was born and raised here in Salt Lake. I know how bad winters can be around here. The weather we've had in January, February, the stuff we're having right now is a miracle. Without the weather that we have had, I don't think we could have made it. I really don't."

Gary Barlow, President of J & S Mechanical and one of the Conference Center project's largest subcontractors and suppliers, gave his perspective:

"You know, I don't remember who contacted us initially, but because of the things we'd done prior probably with Layton and with the church, somehow we got contacted to do some budget estimating to help the Legacy group come up with estimates, man power loading and all those things. That was 4 or 5 months before we bid the job. So

we spent a considerable amount of time with our people and some sub contractors just to develop some kind of a time frame and man power loads to help out. That was our initial look at it. We were invited on the bid list and there were only 4 bidders. It was a large mechanical project and it had to be bonded. Right now our contract is in excess of $25 million. So it's been a massive undertaking in the time frame.

"We've got great superintendents. Clayne Robinson was our project manager and he did an excellent job. And Jack Jensen was our superintendent. And we had a corp of superintendents involved. Superior Sheet Metal did our sheet metal work. Their contract was in excess of $10 million. They were professional and did a great job under tough circumstances. The largest duct work in that assembly area was 101 inches in diameter. You can walk through that stuff. It's amazing when you get down on the bottom and look up, you think you're looking at a piece of two foot duct work. But the duct work was a huge undertaking and it had to be installed in compliment with the steel. It was hard as the structure went up because of the positioning and the heights, which were

> "The weather we've had these last couple of seasons is a miracle."

in the 100 foot range. I take my hat off to Superior Sheet Metal and our other sub contractor Insulation Systems. They performed all the insulation and did a great job for us as well. It's all people. We were supplying 125 or 130 individuals, just for our portion of the mechanical work, while Superior and Insulation Systems had about 100 men on the job.

"As it is with any downtown project, material handling is a nightmare. Until we got space in the parking structure we tried to have daily deliveries, and no more than weekly deliveries at most to keep our material to a

minimum. Even when we were given the parking structure areas, we could only put so much material down there. The air handlers were huge and there were a lot of them. They go in confined spaces. A lot of them had to be taken to Chicago Bridge and Iron and left there, until they were going to be ready to be placed on the job. Then they were loaded in trucks back to the project so that we could install them as the project went along. That was a major effort with material.

"The church builds everything to 150 year standards, to last a long time, so all the materials are top grade, all the concrete you see is extra thick. And in areas where a core cut is necessary, sometimes we'd be drilling through a 2-foot steel beam. There are a lot of those type of obstacles to overcome as you are installing and doing the work. I just take my hat off to our guys. Jack Jensen was our main superintendent, and I had Lyle Edwards handle the fountains.

"The fountain system for the church was huge— in excess of $1,300,000, just for the fountain system on the piping and the pumps we installed. We had a superintendent to deal strictly with the routing and everything that had to take place to feed up to the roof structure. John Summerfeld was one of our superintendents; it was an undertaking with many key individuals.

"We did the total mechanical which included all the

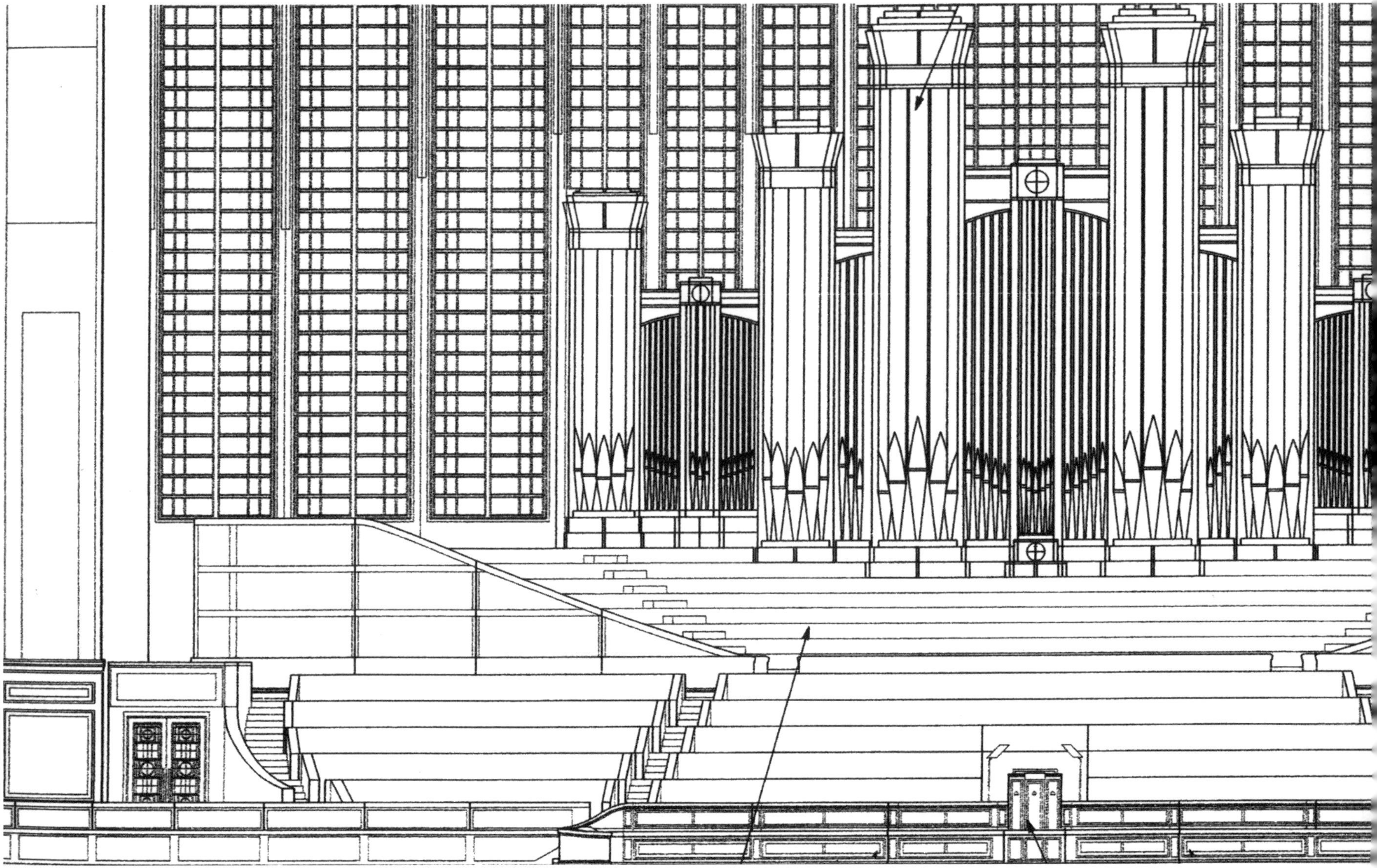

fountain piping, HVAC piping, duct work and all the insulation portions of the project. As a member of the LDS Church, it was really a wonderful opportunity for me and my dad, Jim Barlow, our head estimator. When it comes to the real big jobs, he's the one. I know he is the best estimator in Salt Lake. I just know he is the one that really put the bulk of the job together and took care of it, as he does with all our big projects. So we depended heavily on his expertise.

"I said as we were going through this thing, President Hinckley must have been inspired of the Lord to have this done. Because if it gets done, it is a miracle within itself that it has happened. Everything that has taken place has been in such a quick time frame. There were so many change orders and RFI and change conditions. When you're doing a fast track job that is that huge there are continual things that have to be worked out and changes made. We'd have to switch directions and move in another way right in the

middle of things. That was a difficult part of it.

"I think we're down right now to about 20 men and the heat has been on for some time now. All of our rough in work will be complete, registers and grills and plumbing fixtures by the 15th of this month. They still have us doing changes. But we're really on target and we're hoping that we can set the fixtures to meet the deadlines; we can't put them in without tile and paint and everything else. We've been able to cut back, but we were so fortunate to have such good people involved, even from our plumber and our pipe fitters and welders. We just had really dedicated good people. We were on overtime for a long time. We've worked an overtime schedule out that doesn't kill our guys. We work four 10-hour days and an 8-hour day, which gives the workers overtime, but they get their Friday off and their weekend. It refreshes them and enables them to work. When you're doing a months of overtime, it's hard on everyone. There is a point where there are diminishing returns.

"When you bid a job like this you are nervous and your stomach is in knots. You wonder if you've got everything covered and you wonder if you should do it. Legacy's George Ambrose placed a call to me a couple days before—'We need you on the job type call.' That was really neat coming from him because we really liked the partner group up there.

"One last comment, without Harvey Wright the

overall construction supervisor, that job would never have been built. He is one sharp guy. He is tireless for his age. In all honesty, if they gave anybody an accolade for that project, it ought to be Harvey Wright."

Dick Shipley is one of the senior construction supervisors for Legacy Constructors. He has worked in the construction industry in Utah for more than 25 years.

"This has been the most challenging job that I have ever worked on during my forty-seven years in construction. We have been sprinting a long time. When we first started putting in footings we were on six days a week, ten hours a day, and that really hasn't changed much over the two years. There has not been a lot of time for personal and family time. In spite of the stress on everyone, we've had good rapport on this job with very little bickering. That is a big accomplishment, it's almost a miracle.

"I meet with Tom Hanson and the architect for the Church every other week over at the Joseph Smith Building. People over here were putting in a lot of hours and not getting a lot of recognition for the work they were doing. A pat on the back goes a long ways.

"So one day when I was meeting with Tom, he happened to make the comment that, We really appreciate what you guys are doing over there. And my comment back to Tom was, Tom, the people in this room understand that. The people that are in the trenches working out there

are the people that need to know that.

"It wasn't long after that President Hinckley himself came over here. He had to come to make some decision, but he spent enough time that he was able to shake hands with maybe 100 fellows on this job. I have people coming up to me, even as we speak, and this has been a year ago, telling me what a thrill it was to be able to shake hands with the Prophet. In fact, I was with Tom Hanson and the entire First Presidency had come over to make a decision on a particular paver that was going to be around the building. I had put the pavers together so I was concerned about which one they would choose. Well, I was standing probably 30 feet away from President Hinckley and Tom Hanson came up to me and he said, 'Dick, by the way, have you ever met the President?' I said, 'Oh sure, when would I meet the President?' And he said, 'Well, you're going to meet him now.' He brought President Hinckley right over and it was in the middle of winter and it was ice cold. The President had gloves on to try and keep his little frail hands warm. And I'll tell you the first thing he did was take that glove off and shake hands with me. Pretty exciting."

WEATHER FACTS
courtesy of Mark Eubank (KSL Weather)

- January 1998, January 1999, and January 2000 were all warmer than a normal February.

- January is normally the snowiest month of the year and January 1996 had 63 inches of snow (254% of normal). January 1997, 1998, 1999, and 2000 were all normal or below normal for snowfall.

- Winter is defined meteorologically as the period December 1 through February 28. The warmest six consecutive winters ever measured in Salt Lake City (since 1847) occurred from 1994 to 1999.

- The last really cold-snowy December was 8 years ago. The last really cold-snowy January was 7 years ago. The last really cold-snowy February was 4 years ago.

April 1999.

161

April 1999.

May 4, 1999.

June 1, 1999.

August 1999.

October 1999.

November 1999.

November 1999.

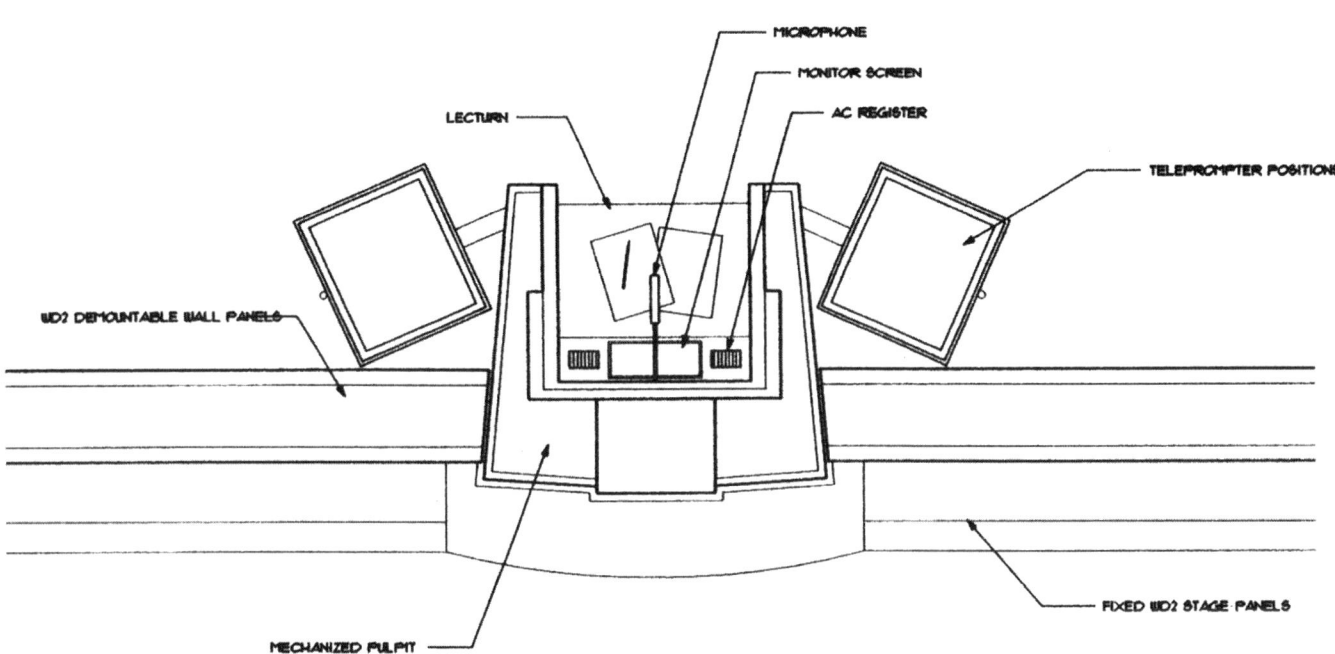

CHAPTER FOUR

2000
SPRINT TO THE FINISH

As the year 1999 was coming to a close and the Conference Center appeared no where near being ready for the promised opening for LDS General Conference on April 1, 2000, Ted M. Jacobsen, one of the Legacy Constructors partners made this insightful comment:

"The Conference Center will be completed when President Hinckley wanted it completed; that's a miracle. There are a lot of dads who have missed a lot of soccer games and a lot of dinners. You can do that for a few weeks, but eventually it gets very wearing physically and emotionally. We've had some long days and some long hours. Now it's the sprint to the finish line and I think we'll make it!

"The workers who have worked on this building understand that this is a once in a lifetime experience. I hope after the dust settles that they will look with pride to what they've done. It's going to be a striking and handsome

FACTS & STATS

- 8,000 organ pipes total (170 visible in front display).
- Largest pipe is 18 inches in diameter and 39 feet tall, the smallest is the size of a pencil.
- Organ case manufactured and installed by Fetzers' Inc. of Salt Lake City.
- Organ pipes and components built by Schoenstein & Company of San Francisco.
- The organ console has 5 keyboards, one pedal keyboard, and 200 stop controls.
- Fountains and water features circulate 6,000 gallons of water each minute.
- Landscaped roof includes 2,000 trees, 6 acres of grass, bushes, and wild flowers with an automated irrigation and drainage system.

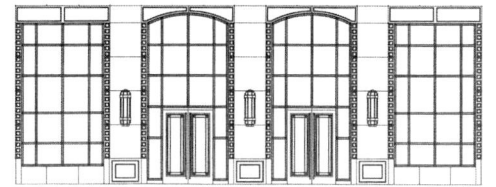

building, one that will endure and last. I hope people never forget that it's built by human beings who place the rebar and nail the nail. A building like this is built on the backs and in the minds of the craftsmen and those who supervise them."

The New York Times featured the following article by Gustav Niebuhr on Sunday, February 6, 2000:

"In October 1867, when the now-famous Mormon Tabernacle opened, members of the Church of Jesus Christ of Latter-day Saints created a traffic jam of horse-drawn carts on nearby dirt streets as they arrived for the first church conference held within.

> "A building like this is built on the backs and in the minds of the craftsmen and those who supervise them."

Inside, under a ceiling supported by hand-hewn beams and wooden pegs, the Mormon prophet, Brigham Young, marveled at being able to speak to so many people— 6,000 bunched together on pine-wood pews— under a single roof.

In two months, in a historically resonant move, the church will open a vast new Conference Center to replace the venerable Tabernacle as a site for the semiannual church conferences. The new building's great size and technological sophistication offer symbolic testimony to how far Mormonism has come from being a frontier faith to a global religion. The church is entering its

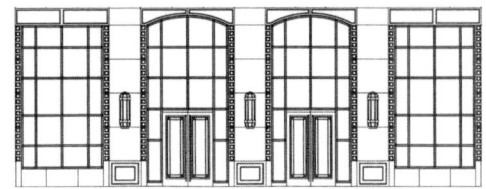

third century with nearly 11 million members, more of them outside the United States than within, the result in large part of the proselytizing of 60,000 young missionaries.

"The Conference Center has risen on a 10-acre city block across from Temple Square, home to the Tabernacle, with its rounded roof, and the Salt Lake City Temple. Sheathed in local granite and designed with straight lines and right angles, it rises about 70 feet above street level. Its roof is being landscaped as a park, with alpine grasses and flowers, aspens and evergreens, and a channel through which water will flow to the building's front and cascade down in a waterfall.

"But the most impressive dimension lies within the 1.4 million-square-foot interior, where an auditorium of 21,000 seats makes the center one of the world's largest religious buildings."

The miracle that was spoken of by so many of the Conference Center workers was indeed accomplished! The 21,000-seat auditorium and public entrance areas were ready for the sessions of LDS General Conference on April 1-2, 2000. During the two-day conference more than 100,000 members attended the sessions held in the new center. Most were awestruck by the size and beauty of the auditorium and finished areas of the building.

President Hinckley's remarks as the first speaker of the first session of General Conference on April 1, 2000 were as follows:

"My dearly beloved brethren and sisters, what a

Interior of Conference Center auditorium.

magnificent sight you are, this vast congregation of Latter-day Saints gathered together in this new and wonderful hall. The organ is not completed, and there are various construction details yet to be attended to. But fortunately the work is far enough along that we are able to use it for this conference. A year or so ago in speaking concerning it, I expressed the opinion that we may not be able to fill it initially. It seats three and a half times the capacity of the Tabernacle. But already we are in trouble. People are filling all of the seats.

"During the four general sessions and the priesthood session we will be able to accommodate about 100,000. We had requests for 370,000 tickets. . . . So many wanted to attend this first conference in the new hall. Unfortunately, that is impossible. I was somewhat shocked to learn that the people from my own ward, who are nearby and whom I love, have received no tickets.

"The building of this structure has been a bold undertaking. We worried about it. We prayed about it. We listened for the whisperings of the Spirit concerning it. And only when we felt the confirming voice of the Lord did we determine to go forward.

"The vision of a new hall was clearly in mind. Various

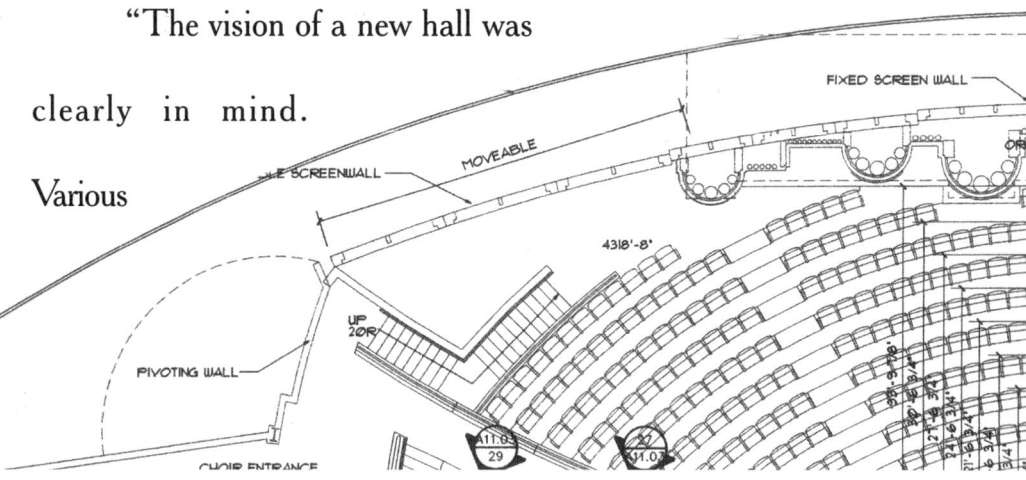

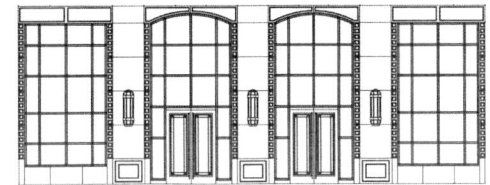

architectural schemes were studied. One was finally selected. It included a massive structure to seat 21,000 with a theater accommodating another thousand. There would not be interior pillars to obstruct the view of the speaker. There would be trees and running water on the roof.

"It will prove to be a great addition to this city. Not only will our general conferences be held here, and some other religious meetings, but it will serve as a cultural center for the very best artistic presentations. We hope that those not of our faith will come here, experience the ambience of the beautiful place, and feel grateful for its presence. We thank all who have worked so hard to bring it to this stage— the architects, with whom we have had many meetings; the general contractors, three of whom have worked together; the subcontractors; and the hundreds of craftsmen who have labored here; the construction supervisor; the city building inspectors; and everyone who has had a hand in this project. They have all joined in a herculean effort so that we might meet together this morning...." (Ensign, May 2000, 4-6)

This was truly a great and historic day in the eyes of those who had caught President Hinckley's vision and sense of urgency concerning the completion of the Conference Center.

Seating arrangement for the LDS Church Mormon Tabernacle Choir.

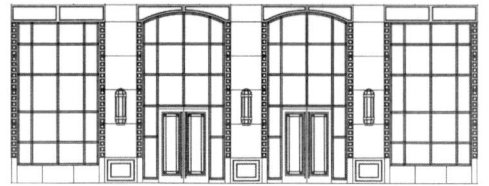

PRESIDENT HINCKLEY'S WALNUT TREE

As part of his opening day remarks, President Hinckley referred to the story of the very pulpit from which he was speaking:

"And now, my brothers and sisters, I would like to tell you about another feature of this wonderful building. If I get a little personal and even a little sentimental, I hope you will forgive me. I love trees. When I was a boy we lived on a farm in the summer, a fruit farm. Every year at this season we planted trees. I think I have never missed a spring since I was married, except for two or three years when we were absent from the city, that I have not planted trees at least one or two—fruit trees, shade trees, ornamental trees, and spruce, fir, and pine among the conifers. I love trees.

"Well, some 36 years ago I planted a black walnut. It was in a crowded area where it grew straight and tall to get the sunlight. A year ago, for some reson it died. But walnut is a precious furniture wood. I called Brother Ben Banks of the

Seventy, who, before giving his full time to the Church, was in the business of hardwood lumber. He brought his two sons, one a bishop and the other recently released as a bishop and who now run the business, to look at the tree. From all they could tell it was solid, good, and beautiful wood. One of them suggested that it would make a pulpit for this hall. The idea excited me.

"The end product is beautiful. I wish all of you could examine it closely. It represents superb workmanship, and here I am speaking to you from the tree I grew in my backyard, where my children played and also grew.

President Hinckley and his walnut tree (Courtesy of Mrs. Jane H. Dudley)

"It is an emotional thing for me. I have planted another black walnut or two. I will be long gone before they mature. When that day comes and this beautiful pulpit has grown old, perhaps one of them will do to make a replacement. To Elder Banks and his sons, Ben and Bradley, and to the skilled workers who have designed and built this, I offer my profound thanks for making it possible to have a small touch of mine in this great hall where the voices of prophets will go out to all the world in testimony of the Redeemer of mankind." (Ensign, May 2000, 6)

The following are the comments made by Ben E. Banks and Bradley Banks on January 12, 2000 about that same black walnut tree:

"Early last spring, Dad (Elder Ben B. Banks) was in President Hinckley's office on Church matters after which President Hinckley asked Dad, 'Would you and your boys come up and take a look at a walnut tree in my backyard? I think it's

(Courtesy of W. Dee Halverson)

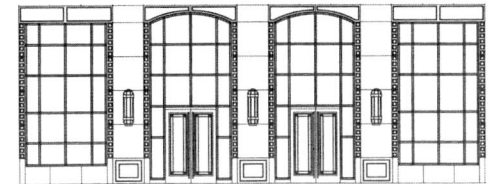

dying and I'd like to know if there is any value to it.' So we went up there on a Saturday.

"President Hinckley showed us the tree, we could see that it was indeed dying, if not already dead. Practically all of the walnut trees along the Wasatch Front have been killed by a bore in the last few years. President Hinckley wanted to know if there was any commercial value to it. And I said, 'You know, President, rather than looking at the commercial value, you have a reputation for being the building prophet. Why don't we cut this tree down and use the lumber to build the podium or pulpit in the new Conference Center? Since that is really part of your legacy.' And he lit up and said, 'That's a great idea!' So that's how we proceeded. We got a company in there to cut the tree down."

Bradley Banks continued the story:

"The main goal here was to get the tree down without destroying the house. We didn't know if there would be sufficient wood or quality to do anything with it. But we told the prophet that we'd get it down and get it into the saw mill and see what the quality was and what we could harvest out of it. I had several tree services come and look at it and they were all very concerned about getting it down without dropping it on the house. I found one that didn't have any qualms at all and they sent out a crew of climbers.

"We had a 40 or 50 foot tree to work with. The top

section had to be cut into small pieces that the climbers could manhandle down to the ground. We were able to harvest the twenty-foot trunk of the tree in two pieces and we laid that down in his yard. The branches all went into the grinder. We were able to pull the two big sections away from the house and got them into a truck. And we brought them down to our lumber yard.

"When we got it cut up, I took a few samples up to President Hinckley's office and he was very excited about it and anxious to see the quality and quantity. I told him that a man at the saw mill had given me some interesting information. He said that when we grow walnut in the West, where it's not a native tree, it usually grows up a short distance and then sprouts branches and starts going from there. You get a short tree with a lot of branch, or head, as it reaches out for sunshine to grow. He said, 'Something has happened with this tree. It has been grown in a location where there has been no sunshine. When that happens, instead of branching out, the tree just shoots straight up and up and up searching for sunshine.'

"In President Hinckley's back yard, the tree had grown up against the house. It was surrounded by tall, mature pine trees on the east side. The only time it got sunshine was at high noon, so it became a tall slender tree, rather than a short fat tree. That is ideal for lumber. Every time you get a branch in a tree, that creates a knot and that

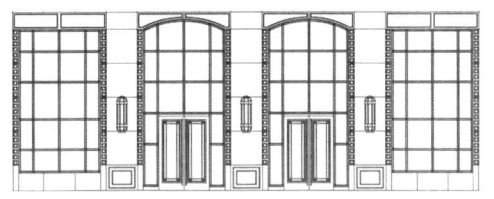

Handcrafted beehive detail for pulpit.
(Courtesy of W. Dee Halverson)

downgrades the quality of lumber. The fact that this little sapling was planted in a place that was difficult to grow, caused it to grow into a good quality piece of lumber. Now that's not to say that it is the number one piece of lumber ever grown, but for what grows in this area, it grew real straight and tall, free of knots and flaws or defects. The challenge of finding sunshine created a piece of wood that was usable thirty-five years down the road. We counted the growth rings and we pulled thirty-five growth rings off it, give or take a year. President Hinckley probably planted that young sapling in about 1964, and thirty-six years later he got a pulpit."

THE NEW ORGAN

One of the early questions about the Conference Center was concerning whether or not the new building would have an organ like the Tabernacle and become the new home for the Mormon Tabernacle Choir. After much discussion it was first decided that the Conference Center would not have an organ and would not be a new venue for the choir— that decision was reversed. Plans began for the design, fabrication and installation of a magnificent organ to match the unusual acoustical needs of the Conference Center.

Leland Gray gave us insight regarding this phase of the planning:

"We were talking to Gerald Ottley at the beginning of our planning explaining the size of the Conference Center. I said, 'You think its a challenge working with a huge choir? Think about turning around and directing 21,000 people.' And he said, 'I'm not going to use my baton. I'm going to use a starting pistol.'

"At the groundbreaking on the site, I was sitting right next to Wendell Smoot, president of the Mormon

Tabernacle Choir. During President Hinckley's talk, Wendell was sitting there kind of downcast thinking that there wasn't an organ planned for the new building. Then President Hinckley announced that the building would have a world-class pipe organ. Wendell pokes me in the ribs and said grinning from ear to ear, 'Did you hear that?. And I said, 'Yes Wendell, I heard it.' And then a moment later, the President said, 'We've decided to let the choir pay for half of it.' Wendell turns to me and he says, 'What did he say?'"

Mr. Jack Bethards of the Schoenstein Organ Company of San Francisco was among the team of specialists charged with the responsibility of creating an organ to fit the requirements unique to the Conference Center organ. He commented on this challenge in December 1999:

"Our association with the Church and the Tabernacle goes back a long way. The Schoenstein Organ Company was founded in 1877 so we've done a fair amount of work over the years, but the big association really started

in the late 1940's when the old Tabernacle organ was moved to BYU and we handled that move. Later we helped in the installation of the new Tabernacle organ in 1949. There are some parts of the old, old organ in the main Tabernacle organ, but in 1949 it was such a massive job that we sort of call it the new organ.

"This Conference Center project is the most challenging job I think any organ builder has been faced with in the 20th century. It's very, very tricky. The auditorium is the largest ever designed by double. It has a totally different acoustical picture, and we're working in all new territory that has never been explored before; how to make music sound good in a building this big.

"Our objective is to make an organ that is about the same loudness as the present Tabernacle organ, because it's a perfect balance with the Tabernacle Choir, and the main job of the organ is to accompany them. The organ will have the same sonic power as the Tabernacle organ. Christopher Jaffe's acoustical system will help bring the sound out to the far reaches of the hall.

"All three Tabernacle organists, the acousticians, and Fetzer's, and the Church architects have worked with us on the organ design. It's taken a huge amount of careful study. This organ is not intended by the Church to be a replacement or to overshadow in any way the Tabernacle organ. That is important. The Tabernacle is the musical

center of the Church worldwide. It will continue to be the location of the weekly choir broadcasts. This new organ is for use at General Conference.

"There are a lot of special elements in designing an organ for choir accompaniment. We've tried to incorporate every single effect that you'd ever need to accompany the choir in all kinds of music, from the most serious to the most popular.

"The general authorities of the LDS Church felt that the symbolism of having an organ with pipes was very important to give the building a religious aura. It is a reminder that this is not just a big stadium or arena, but it is a building with religious usage. They also insisted that it be a true pipe organ.

"There are two basic types of organ pipe construction; metal and wood. The wood pipes are generally made of poplar and sugar pine with some other hard woods in certain places. The metal pipes are made of tin, lead, zinc and in some cases copper. Most of them are an alloy of about half tin and half lead, but the front pipes are made mostly of zinc. This is a very specialized organ. The biggest challenge is just the size and breadth of it. It's a big, big piece of equipment!"

Paul Fetzer was also one of the team of experts charged with designing, fabricating, and installing the Conference Center organ. Here is his account of that project

given on January 12, 2000:

"Fetzer's was founded in 1909 by my grandfather, Casper J. Fetzer, who was a German immigrant. My father John K. Fetzer and my uncle Percy Fetzer grew the company into a much larger firm and Richard Fetzer, our president and my brother Wallace Fetzer, have continued with a reputation for quality. In 1915, my grandfather built the organ wing additions to the original Tabernacle organ. I have had the opportunity with Brother Cundick to help coordinate the wood construction and the embellishments on the Assembly Hall organ, which has intricate filigree. With this history it is a great experience to work on the organ case and rostrum for the new Conference Center.

"The design team consisted of Lee Gray, who was the head of the team from the LDS Church, and a fellow by the name of Stewart Goodwin, an organ builder out of San Bernadino, California, who did a lot with the pipe arrangements. He is also a very talented organ tuner and has worked for years on the Tabernacle organ. In addition, we had Scott Bleak, from the Church's staff who did some of the fundamental thinking on the organ and was a great help in doing all the layouts and establishing the positioning of the organ. Jack Bethards and his staff were invaluable in the design of the organ. My role at first was to coordinate the woodwork of the organ and that grew into interpreting the woodwork to its form as it stands today.

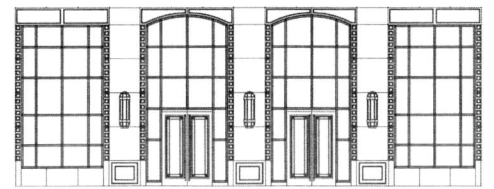

"The idea of the large towers was originally to mimic somewhat the shape of the Tabernacle organ. But on further review we found that it was looking too much like the Tabernacle organ and Lee Gray's staff came up with the idea of putting arches over the organ. Simultaneously, Stewart Goodwin expressed the need to put a roof to capture the sound within the organ so it was not lost in the vast ceiling of the new Conference Center. He wanted the sound moved forward into the microphones which would then carry the sound by transmission to the rest of the hall. This was accomplished by putting a roof structure from the facade of the organ to the back wall, at such an angle as would express the sound forward through the pipes and through

Worker in Port Townsend, Washington using wooden boat craftsmanship on the Conference Center's unique organ sound reflectors. (Courtesy of Peninsula [Washington] Daily News)

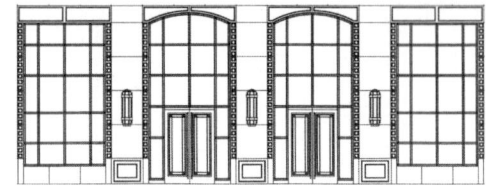

the organ structure itself. Everything on the organ either became transparent to sound or reflective to the sound being produced in the organ itself.

"One of the interesting structures of the organ is the underside of the arches, which express the sound forward. Mr. Goodwin made the suggestion that we should express the sound the way it leaves the mouth of a bugle or a horn. One Saturday as I was working independently of Mr. Goodwin, we both came up with the same idea, to make larger reflective structures on the underside of the organ arches. We called each other on Monday morning and said, 'Hey, I've got this idea,' we were both very enthused to hear each other confirm the fact that the sound needed to be expressed forward and out, not focused such as a cone or round structure might do. We decided to create large curved structures which would mimic the mouth of a horn.

"I started thinking about how to form those structures. It so happened that I was investigating boat building at that particular time and got in contact with a boat lumber supply company in Anacortes, Washington, who referred me to the Northwestern School of Wooden Boat Building in Port Townsend, Washington, on the peninsula north of Tacoma and directly across from Seattle. Those folks were very helpful in instructing us on how we might be able to build structures for the organ that were

stout enough to act as arches which would hold the cornices up. At the same time they must be thick enough to be reflectors for the sound of the organ pipes below.

"Justin Losee of our firm made a visit to the school for boat building and got together with some contractors in the area and finally contracted with Ed Louchard of Louchard Yacht Restoration Company to build these five huge magnificent arches. The center arch is 14 feet long, 6 feet deep and three feet high, made out of inch and a quarter thick solid cherry wood. The other arches are of similar construction. Each slat of cherry wood in the arch tapers from large to small and is also doubled from front to back to form the beautiful boat shaped structures. We originally conceived those to look like the belly of a harp or the back of a lute. In other words, bring a musical connotation as well as an actual physical reflective structure.

"People came from all around the peninsula to see these being built and the local newspaper there called the *Peninsula News* ran an article on the boat-like structures for our organ. There is a little sign attached to the back of the largest boat structure and everyone who worked on them has his signature attached. They'll be immortalized there. If you could ever stand directly on top of the organ, you would see the sign that is attached to the large arc. Jack Bethards was very helpful in helping us come to resolution on the design. We wanted it to be very musical and lyrical

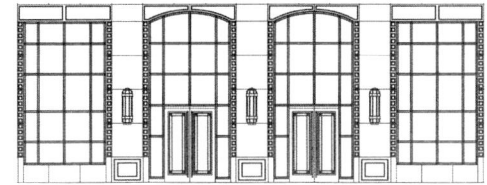

looking, an organ that looked like it's function.

"The interior of an organ is a beautiful thing to an organ builder and has an amazing array of pipes and various structures and flats and rows. We have three structures which are called "clock towers" in organ building. Those three structures have ornaments on them which are in sort of a sun burst shape. They consist of a rippled sycamore veneer and cherry veneer, and they are also expressive in that they reflect the sound produced by the pipe below.

"The wood veneer on the organ case is very interesting and beautiful. The veneer is from a really astounding cherry wood log that was found by Lee Gray and my brother Wallace as they made trips to veneer mills in the East. The wooden organ case veneer is put together in such a way to accentuate the beautiful grain of that cherry log.

"This particular cherry tree was grown in northern Pennsylvania, not far from the village of Harmony and the Susquehanna River. It grew to more than forty inches in diameter and we call it a one-in-a-million veneer log."

AN ACOUSTICAL MASTERPIECE

Leonard Auerbach is President of Auerbach and Associates of San Francisco, California. His firm, Theatre and Media Facilities Design, was among the team of special consultants retained by the Church to help design and outfit the Conference Center with the latest in acoustical and theatrical technology. The following is his perspective as related on December 22, 1999:

"I was involved with the Conference Center project long before the architect was on board, working with Lee Gray and Kerry Nielsen, who I met at a Harvard seminar. They asked me to look at something that they were doing. The germs of this project were just evolving and we started discussing some of the physical aspects of dealing with an audience this large. Typically a large scale audience assembly space is a sports arena that has been converted for various kinds of performances, for instance an ice show or a rock concert. Arenas have the feeling of an athletic environment, and they are all very hard and cold spaces, because of their primary function, supporting sports events. We felt this would be inappropriate for what the LDS

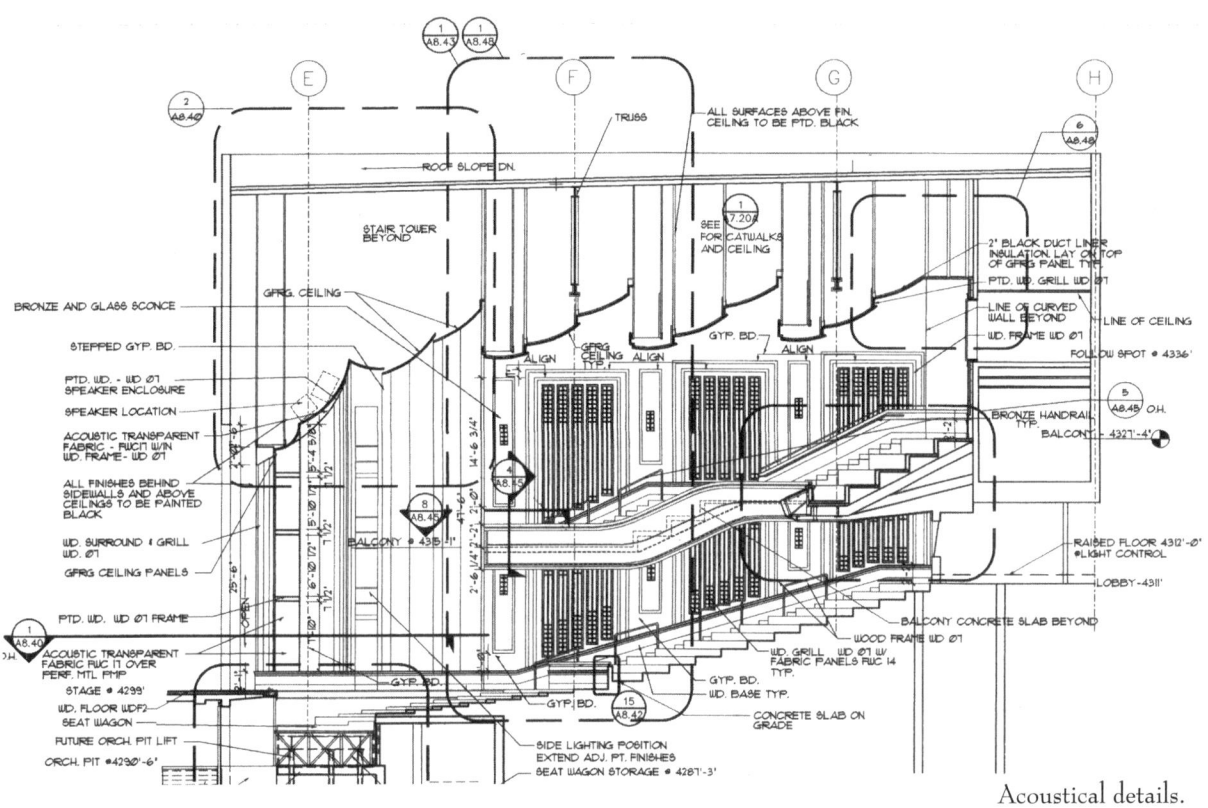

Acoustical details.

"Lee and Kerry took me and my partners to Palmyra, New York and we became familiar with the LDS Church so that we could appreciate what the Church was and what it stood for. That was very important. I remember every time we met with a different committee from the Church or the design team, I kept saying, 'You have to understand the scale of this space in order to understand how it has to be very carefully Church stood for and the image of the Tabernacle and the other facilities that the Church has. We decided to make this building something unto itself.

controlled.' We tried to create an apparent intimacy in a huge space. To give people a real sense of scale, we went to the web site of Boeing Aircraft and downloaded a drawing of a 747. We tucked it in the building neatly without any part of the aircraft touching anything in the building, from wing tip to wing tip and stem to stern and tail to landing gear. Someone else came back a few weeks later and took the same drawing and turned the airplane in the plan and could fit two airplanes in there!

"We did a mock up of some stage lighting to test some of our lighting criteria. I stood right where the First Presidency is going to be, right where the pulpit is going to be and sensed the room. I couldn't believe that there were that many seats in it! As a design tool we examined the physiognomy of a human being. We looked at all the Dreyfus drawings and photographs of motion and human proportion. We're bi-peds which means we walk on two feet. Because of that, our vision is downward at a greater angle than it is upward, because our eyebrows are protecting us. We have a certain amount of peripheral vision. We took that geometry and put it at the pulpit to make sure all the angled criteria going up and down and to the sides included every seat in the audience area. So when the President is out there speaking and looking straight ahead, he still is communicating to everybody in all 21,000 seats.

"Pageants and productions are a very important part

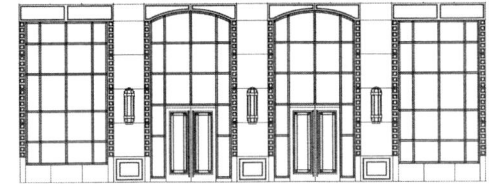

of what this building will do. We're using technology with air bearings to move all the pieces around like a hover craft. We can break down the rostrum and move it away and store it. The front sections of seats are removable as well so that a pageant can come out into the room. One of the things that we noticed in Palmyra, is how guests are immediately greeted by missionaries. There is a major social aspect at the pageant in Palmyra that's really wonderful. It can't happen in the Tabernacle at conference because it's filled completely. So we imposed an aspect of Palmyra in this room. There are two major circulation concourses called cross aisles that are ample enough for that kind of social activity to happen inside. One of the most successful aspects of this space will be the interaction of the audience one to another. There will be room to move and walk and communicate and greet people very easily.

"This is the largest and most sophisticated theatrical lighting system in the world in one facility. In lighting terms the throw distances of where we have to put our lights are quite long. We need quite a few large spotlights in order to properly light the entire rostrum area for television. We're utilizing this system to do this, and we also have some automated lighting that will allow it to change very easily without a lot of labor. We're able to control all of the spaces centrally.

"The small theater, which is a 900 seat legitimate

stage, is going to be fully equipped for dramatic productions and for general conference. It will be a training facility as well as a legitimate theater. The whole building can be run as a single entity or all of the elements can be separated out and work individually. That includes all of the lighting in the lobby spaces and public areas. It will be tremendously effective."

Christopher Jaffe is the Principal-In-Charge for Jaffe Holden Scarbrough Acoustics, Inc. of Norwalk, Connecticut. His firm designed the unique concert hall and speech environments of the Conference Center. He stated on December 22, 1999:

"This is the largest indoor assembly build-ing in the world. A big part of the challenge was the fact that the Church was very concerned about the speech intelligibility during conference. They have spoken in different arenas

In-house broadcasting facilities.

and found it very difficult to obtain good speech intelligibility. There were great concerns about a 21,000 seat facility.

"It was our role to make sure that the overall acoustic environment was such that it would be very suitable for amplified speech, which we would use in such a large venue. That was one of the challenges but the biggest challenge was that conference also entails a musical portion of the program. A new organ is being installed there for the famous Mormon Tabernacle Choir.

"We had the dichotomy of having to provide the right speech environment in the hall, which would mean a very dead hall and almost outdoor-like environment with no reflections, and then to produce a concert hall environment in which we would have reverberations for the musical program. It is difficult to do those things in multi-use theater facilities that seat only 2,000 or 2,500. Here we have to do it in an assembly hall that seats 21,000! We decided to utilize some good physical acoustic practice, architectural acoustic practice in deadening the hall with absorptive materials on the ceiling and the rear walls. We have carpet underneath the seats and we have absorptive seats so that we can keep the reverberations or the reflection patterns down. We are using technology called Electronic Reflective Energy System (ERES).

"The ERES system provides reflections that would

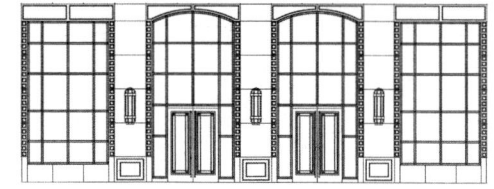

normally be present if we hadn't created such a dead hall and hadn't covered the surfaces with a great deal of absorptive material. A concert hall has a hard wall, and a sound stage for a Hollywood movie would have a very soft wall because they want no reflections. Everything is modified electronically. Here we had the equivalent of a Hollywood sound stage, a very, very dead room. We process the original signal of the choir and the organ and any other instruments through digital signal processing methods, DSP methods, to create reflections coming from the walls and ceilings of the room as if they were hard. In other words, we literally create a virtual room, a different virtual room acoustic from the original through this electronic reflective energy system.

"We have to have a multiplicity of speakers so that we can replicate walls and ceilings, and we process the signals so that it becomes a reflection. There is no source identification with that information just as when you go into a concert hall there is no source identification with a wall. You hear the music coming from the stage but there are these reflections at a certain level and a certain frequency composition arriving to your ear at a certain time. We replicate those."

AN "ALPINE MEADOW" ON THE ROOF

Laurie Olin is the consulting landscape architect for the Conference Center. His firm, Olin Partnership, is based in Philadelphia, Pennsylvania. They designed the "alpine meadow" and fountain system features for the seven-acre roof top. The following is his recollection of that epiphany:

"Our concept for the landscaping on this project began with walking around Salt Lake and thinking about the size of this building and what it was for, and realizing that the building was going to be so large. Bob Frasca, the architect, was talking about 20,000 seats in one room and how to produce something that wouldn't look like a sports facility but would be a house of worship. It was a serious problem. No one has ever done one like it before, you know.

"The Church architects and engineers were wondering how to do a span that big. They looked at domes and thin shells and other structures that had traditionally spanned great distances. When I heard that I said, If you do a structure like a dome, it is going to look so big, it will dwarf the important historic buildings of the

Working on the rooftop landscape.

Tabernacle and the Temple. I was troubled by that because I thought it would get the symbolic meaning of the relationship of the buildings wrong.

"I was thinking that in the early period of the city, agriculture was of such importance. Bob and I walked up to the McCune Mansion to analyze our options. I said, Bob, you can't think of this in terms of a building. That's a funny thing to say to an architect. He is an extremely nice man and very shrewd and he looked at me waiting to see where I was going with this. I said, You really have to

think of this in terms of the landscape. This ten acre roof will be too big, it would dwarf these other important buildings. What we need to do is put a landscape on top of it. I have spent quite a bit of time with my family driving around the Four Corners area. I thought about that landscape. That's it! Make it a piece of the landscape. Have it a building as you approach it from the city, but from uphill, think of it as being a park having to do with Utah. The two of us decided on the spot to make a seven-acre roof that didn't look like a roof.

"We have the sky, water, earth and rocks. The birds and butterflies are going to come. Once we knew how to approach it, the pieces began to fall in place. We gave it some texture and color with evergreens and flowers, and we will irrigate to keep it from looking all burnt out in the hot summers. We want it beautiful in different seasons with a blooming period, but without greenhouses. We chose long plants that get gray and twiggy at certain times of the year and would look good against the stone, with the color and shadows against the building and against the curve of the roof. Those things were really of great importance to our design."

Susan Weiler, Mr. Olin's partner with the Olin Partnership of landscape architects gave this unique insight into the story on December 22, 1999:

"The whole building is landscaped as part of the

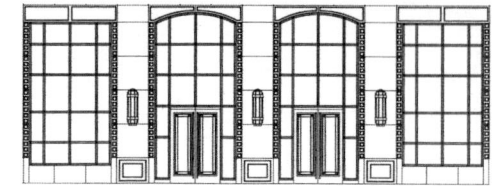

design concept. To do that we worked with the structural engineers to understand what their weight constraints were, not only of the various plant materials, but of the soils, the weight of the water and the fountains and all of the things that are on top of the roof as well.

"It's a fairly sophisticated system of not only the structure but the waterproofing and the insulation, and the soil. In some cases we used foam fill, an insulated fill that takes up some of the voids where we didn't need the depths of the soil for the trees. You need three or four feet of depth for the root ball on the tree. In the meadow we needed a certain depth over the whole meadow to be able to support the meadow. It all needs to be drained and you need access to the water, both the irrigation water and the precipitation that moves through the water. You need to be able to conduct that through the soil or through the drainage layer, and then through the drainage system of the building and up through the civil utilities.

"We were using native materials where we could. We can't re-create nature but we can simulate it. We tried very hard to select materials that would work in this particular environment. We worked fairly closely with Peter Lassig to make sure we used materials that he thought he could maintain well and have the effect that we were looking for with the fountains and the terrace.

"If you consider the entire landscape to be like a

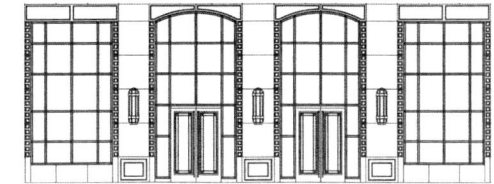

wedding cake and you slice down through it, there are three parts to this wedding cake. One slice of cake goes through planted areas and another one goes through paved areas and another one goes through fountains and water features. If you went through the planted area, you'd find the meadow plants on top. Then you'd find a layer of six or eight inches of a mixture of the growing medium and some organic material, and then you would have the lightweight aggregate soil that was used. The meadow would be 18 inches, then you'd have a layer of a filter fabric and a drainage mat. It does two things. It allows the water to move through, but catches the particles of the soil so that they don't get into the other drainage. You just want the water to be moving through. In the meadow we had a more waffley kind of system, a plastic waffle that acts both as a drainage and in some cases it could actually act as a reservoir as well, and then we have two or three inches of insulation. Then the waterproofing and then the structural deck. Most of the trees are in planters in one way or another, and we tried to have as much root run as possible. We kept at least a foot to 18 inches of soil on top everywhere for the top root run. Around the trees themselves we had a bigger area for the full depth of the three or four feet that it needed for the root ball. In areas where we didn't need that soil and we were trying to lessen the weight, we had big blocks of Styrofoam fill. Under that we put a filter fabric and then a drainage

mat and then a drainage layer of slightly larger aggregates. Then we had the drainage pipe that connects to the drainage system and the insulation and the waterproofing. In most cases the paving is a granite paver, with a setting bed of about an inch, then the structural deck or the topping slab, depending on what the elevations were."

Chris Evans is the supervisor with American Landscaping Company and the man responsible for the massive task landscaping the entire roof of the Conference Center. He said on February 23, 2000:

"We have a six-acre landscaped roof with about 256 mature trees on it and tons of special soil mix. There are about 25,000 yards of soil here that we brought in and

Rooftop landscape.

placed. That's a mountain of soil. Then we put irrigation and sprinklers throughout the whole thing, which has been another challenge of getting from one planter up to the next.

"All together there are over nine hundred trees of all different species on this roof top. We have Serbian Spruce trees, White Fir trees, which are most of the pine trees. Up on the roof there is kind of a unique tree, a Bristle Comb pine. They grow at about 11,000 feet in little groves up in Canada. So that's actually where they have been dug from. We also have Aspen trees up on the roof and then down on the plaza we have Covertaria trees, Golden Rain trees, Elm trees, Red Oak trees and that is quite a variety. The pine trees are probably the heaviest with large root

balls weighing about 3,500 to 4,500 pounds per tree.

"The Conference Center roof landscape will also have acres of native meadow seeded with a huge assortment of wild flowers. But the most satisfying thing for me personally is to know every time I drive down the street, even when I'm 70 years old and can show my grandkids and tell them that I placed trees on the roof and worked to make this a beautiful building."

One of the first questions asked by everyone concerning the landscaping and fountain systems on the Conference Center's roof is: "Isn't there anyone worried about leaks?" Yes, there certainly is! Paul Seppi represents Utah Tile & Roofing and is the waterproofing installer for the entire structure from footings and foundations to the elaborate rooftop with all its irrigation and drainage systems. These were his comments during the spring of 2000:

"Our job is waterproofing the whole building. A brief description is that we try and keep all the water out of this structure, which is a pretty risky part of construction. The rooftop landscaping adds a whole new dimension when you're putting springs, fountains, and water runnels. Although we've had experience with this type of structure before, we are very concerned about the running water and all sorts of issues over the top of this building. We have had more than a few sleepless nights over it.

"The product we have applied is American

HydroTech. It is a hot-apply rubberized asphalt, with a reinforcement built right in. It also has a different system of protection boards, drainage boards and insulation that is applied right along with the product. In other words, the granite paver areas differ in application from the planter areas. There is also a series of plant and tree root barriers that prevent the landscape root systems from damaging the waterproofing membrane applied directly to the building itself. A very elaborate drainage system has been installed, but it has now been covered completely with layers of top soil and plantings.

You will never see our work again, hopefully.

"I think the architects specified the best material available for this roof covering system. This material is a very forgiving membrane because of all the construction traffic that has gone over the rooftop of this building. It gives and stretches quite a bit, but it won't take huge movements.

Rooftop landscaping near spire.

"The entire project on the horizontal surfaces is nearly 400,000 square feet in area. And there are also many thousands of square feet of vertical surfaces, since we started with the footings and foundations which are 100 feet deep in some areas. In total there are more than 700,000 square feet of surface areas that we have waterproofed here at the Conference Center, since we started on this project two years ago. At times we had a crew of up to 50 men working here, but now we will finish up with twenty.

"The most challenging thing has been to create details without a complete set of architectural and engineering plans. Not every little thing was thought through so we had to create solutions as we went along. Another challenge has been the schedule and trying to get the project completed in the time frame allowed. There have been a lot of people working on top of each other, damaging each other's product. But all in all, everybody has been cooperative and I think the project is going to show that.

"It has been a most satisfying thing just to be involved in a project such as this. Hopefully we will be successful in what we have accomplished with our own work on this significant building. Really, this is a one-of-a-kind structure in the whole country. If we can prove this one to be watertight, I think we really have done something special."

FINAL SPRINT TO THE FINISH

Robert Frasca is the Partner in Charge of Design on the Conference Center project. He is a senior partner of the architectural firm Zimmer Gunsul Frasca Partnership in Portland, Oregon. His overview of the project and its numerous unique aspects are related in his comments of January 14, 2000:

"At the very beginning, we were contacted by Lee Gray, who is the Church architect. He asked me if I was interested in working on the Conference Center, and I was. I want to emphasize that Lee and I had a very, very good collaboration from the very beginning, it's continuing now to the completion of the building. That's true of Tom Hanson and the rest of the team at LDS, as well as the contractors. I think we've been able to accomplish a great deal in a very short amount of time and I'm very happy with the result.

"Lee asked me to look at the site and I walked around it very, very carefully. The first idea I had, which was the one that we ended up building, was to take advantage of the 65 foot grade change from the southwest to the northeast. And essentially, make the building as much a park as we could. The whole purpose of that was that a building with

a ten acre footprint, with a 21,000 seat capacity, could have very easily dominated the Temple, which is the icon of the Church of Jesus Christ of Latter-day Saints. Anything that would have diminished that would have been a very serious violation to not only the Temple, but Temple Square and Salt Lake City as a whole. When I proposed that, Lee Gray could really see the wisdom of it.

"We presented it to the First Presidency and it was obvious they felt the same way. We had very strong support for the idea from President Hinckley on down. As we proceeded on the building, some of the key decisions, had to do with the overall quality of it. The Church has had a tradition of building good buildings from the very beginning, whether it was the Tabernacle or the Temple. President Brigham Young, sent his architect to Europe for two or three years before he even started on the design of the Temple. This support and concern for building quality

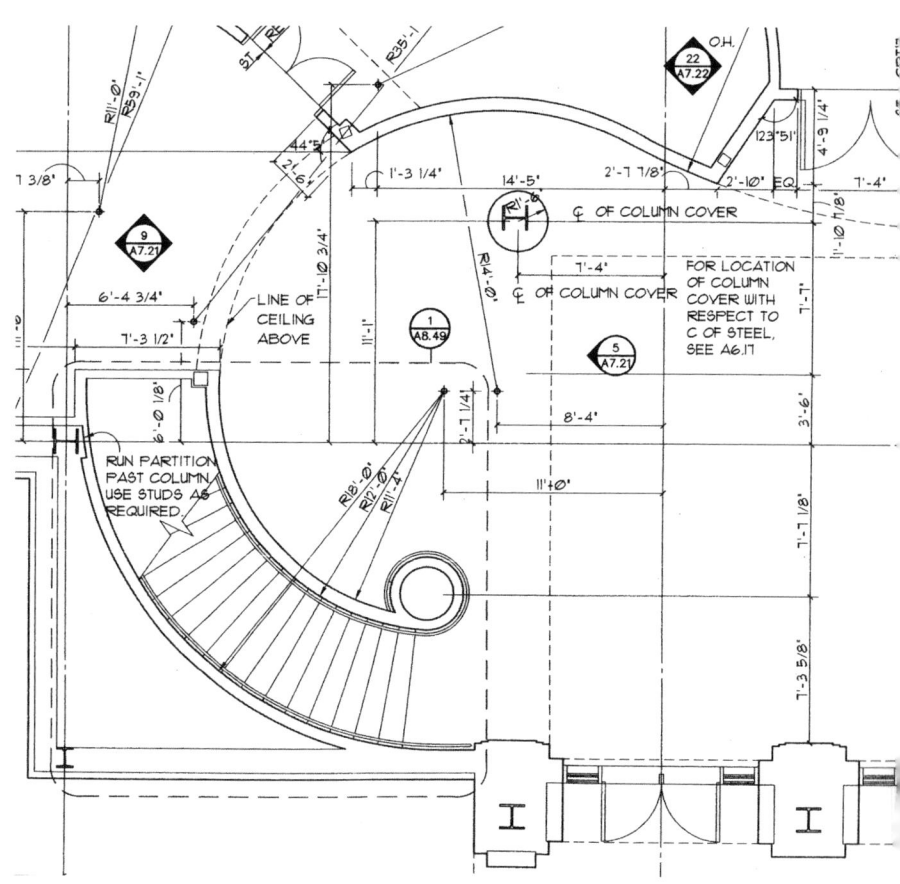

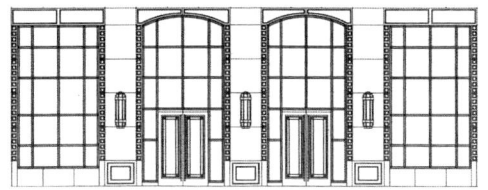

extends to the present day. The result is a building that was part of our original vision. It really pays homage to the Temple and Temple Square, extends Temple Square from being a one block development to a two block development. You really don't see the building all at once. You see it in pieces and the sense is that it's really an extension of Temple Square. The great open space at the southwest that is right on North Temple, extends that feeling. As you're up further to the north where the state capitol is, again you get a sense of this green and open space that comes cascading down. The central figure in the sky are the towers of the Temple. From that aspect, I couldn't be more pleased.

"I think that the interior lobbies are very dignified. They work off of the adjacent streets in very convenient ways and they all lead to the great assembly room, with its focus on the rostrum. One of the icons of the Church has always been the organ. That design has really matured very

Detail from the Little Theater lobby.

beautifully. The room is going to be a very religious space when it's complete. It has the skylights that are going to flood the room with light, which will give it a very reverential character. It will serve a multiplicity of purposes like pageants, as they have in New York and Hawaii, and other activities for the community at large, whether they are members of the Church or not. I think that's a very wonderful way to reach out. It is very much a 21st century building, with the electronic and the acoustics systems state of the art and even beyond.

"I remember one day, I was walking up the street on the north side of the site. A couple of weeks before I had gone through the Church Historical Museum, and there is a very nice model of what Salt Lake looked like in about 1878. You could look out over the valley and see the mountains beyond. I thought, "What an incredible view. Wouldn't it be nice if people could have the same kind of image of what Salt Lake City looks like today." Walking up that street, I said to Laurie, "I think we ought to do a great park on the roof and submerge the building". Being a landscape architect, he agreed.

"The idea of what kind of a park this ought to be matured with conversations that Laurie, Lee Gray and I had together. We wanted to honor the Temple, so the idea emerged of the great stairs that cascade. We talked about having water up there and it seemed like a good idea but there were some concerns about leaking. A member of the Quorum of the Twelve said that the idea of water was very

much part of the tradition of the Church and quoted some scriptures. Therefore that became a very important element. We didn't want to confine it to the top, so we decided on a waterfall. I felt it ought to center on the sidewalk of Temple Square so that as people are walking north, they would be drawn across North Temple to the new Conference Center. Laurie suggested we use some of the natural landscape of the state of Utah, bringing in the wild grasses and so forth. The design is very beautiful and reminds everyone that visits of the tradition of the state of Utah and the great and powerful landscape that exists beyond the confines of the urban areas.

Laurie did a wonderful job.

"We had a very strong collaboration with Len Auerbach and his team from San Francisco. We designed the building from the inside out and outside in, simultaneously. Len and his team as well as our acoustic consultants worked together. We visited the largest auditorium in the world, in Mexico City, which seats about 10,000. We used it as a life size model.

"It's been an opportunity of a lifetime to work on this building. Everyone realized that at the very outset, so everyone worked extremely hard, long hours, and it has represented their best thinking. I would like to commend

them, for their energy and intelligence, and willingness to listen and to collaborate. That is true on everyone's part. Without an incredible amount of cooperation and open mindedness this could never have been accomplished, in terms of time, quality and cost effectiveness. I would like everyone to know that their spirit of collaboration and hard work really paid dividends, and the dividends are shown in the building."

Dick Shipley is one of the senior construction supervisors for Legacy Constructors. He has worked in the construction industry in Utah for more than 25 years.

"This has been the most challenging job that I have ever worked on during my forty-seven years in construction. We have been sprinting a long time. When we first started putting in footings we were on six days a week, ten hours a day, and that really hasn't changed much over the two years. There has not been a lot of time for personal and family time. In spite of the stress on everyone, we've had good rapport on this job with very little bickering. That is a big accomplishment, it's almost a miracle."

January 2000.

January 2000.

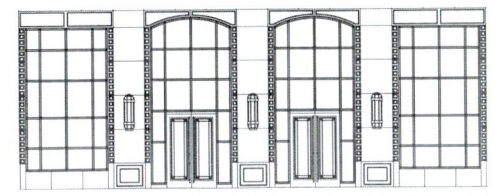

January 2000.

January 2000.

January 2000.

February 2000.

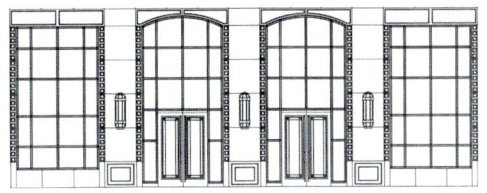

February 2000.

February 2000.

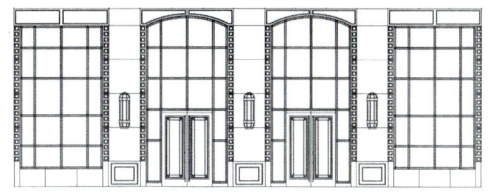

February 2000.

May 2000.